SOME ASPECTS OF CRYSTAL FIELD THEORY

D1282410

SOME ASPECTS OF

HARPER'S CHEMISTRY SERIES

STUART A. RICE, Editor

CRYSTAL
FIELD
THEORY /

THOMAS M. DUNN
> *Department of Chemistry, University of Michigan*

DONALD S. McCLURE
> *Institute for the Study of Metals, University of Chicago*

RALPH G. PEARSON
> *Department of Chemistry, Northwestern University*

HARPER & ROW, PUBLISHERS, NEW YORK

CONTENTS

PREFACE

In the past ten years the concepts and uses of the crystal and ligand field approximations have had their impact upon nearly every chemistry department in Europe and North America. Also with this passage of time has come a new jargon and the use of the crystal field concepts at a purely qualitative level even in the undergraduate classes.

Both of these developments have been accompanied by the usual danger of too rapid incorporation into basic teaching courses without even the most elementary quantitative treatment, thereby making it difficult for students to grasp the basic principles and nomenclature of the methods.

When the Chemistry Department of the University of Michigan invited me in 1962 to give a series of seminars, it seemed to me appropriate to cover some aspects of the theories at a quantitative level such that they could be followed by most graduate students. The topics chosen were the spectral, magnetic, thermodynamic, and chemical kinetic aspects of crystal field theory, in order that some broad coverage and perspective could be achieved.

Dr. D. S. McClure of the University of Chicago and Dr. R. G. Pearson of Northwestern University kindly consented to give the thermodynamic and kinetic seminars respectively and it was left to me to give the introductory theoretical treatment followed by a discussion of the spectra and magnetism of inorganic complexes.

The form of the talks has been almost completely preserved in this publication except insofar as some extra clarifying detail (necessary in print but, fortunately, not always in the lecture) and some continuity in notation have been added. It is hoped that the informal character of the series, which seemed to be an asset to those who participated in it, has thereby been retained and that this lack of rigor, in parts, does not detract too much from the overall structure of its presentation in printed form.

I would like to thank the Chemistry Department of the University of Michigan and the Institute of Science and Technology for making the series possible.

T.M.D.

ACKNOWLEDGMENT

Appreciation and acknowledgment is expressed to the 1962 Class of The University of Michigan for establishing an Institute of Science and Technology publishing fund. This fund has aided in the publication of this work.

SOME ASPECTS OF CRYSTAL FIELD THEORY

CHAPTER 1 THEORETICAL ASPECTS

THOMAS M. DUNN

A. ATOMIC SUMMARY

Since many transition metal complexes behave much like free ions in their spectroscopic and magnetic effects it is necessary to briefly review the concepts of atomic structure and atomic spectra.

(i) Atomic Structure (1, 2, 3, 4, 5)

For most purposes in this discussion it is sufficient to consider the four quantum numbers to be those usually denoted by n, l, m_l, m_s, i.e., the principal, azimuthal, magnetic, and spin quantum numbers. The principal quantum number n, as its name implies, is the principal index of the energy of an electron and n takes all integral values from unity to infinity (at which stage the electron has been ionized from the atom).
Also

$$l = 0, 1, 2, \ldots n - 1$$

$$m_l = -l, -l + 1, \ldots 0 \ldots + l$$

$$m_s = \pm \tfrac{1}{2}$$

and those electrons with $l = 0, 1, 2, 3, 4$ are known by the labels s, p, d, f, g, respectively. Thus the hydrogen atom in its ground state is represented by the symbol $1s^1$, or simply $1s$, and this is called the *atomic configuration*. When there

1

is more than one electron the atomic quantum numbers are defined as

$$L = \sum_i l_i \qquad M_L = \sum_i (m_l)_i \qquad S = \sum_i m_s$$

and the *spin multiplicity*

$$r = 2S + 1$$

Thus for the hydrogen atom with configuration $1s$

$$L = \sum_i l_i = 0$$

and this is denoted by S (as for a single electron only with S).

$$S = \sum_i s_i = \tfrac{1}{2}$$

and

$$r = 2S + 1 = 2$$

The ground *term* of the atom is written $^r L$, i.e., $^2 S$. If the electron were in an excited orbital, say, $n = 2$, $l = 1$, then the *configuration* would be $2p^1$, or just $2p$, and the term would be written $^2 P$, since $\sum l = 1$.

For atoms with more than one electron in the same subshell, e.g., carbon has a configuration $1s^2 2s^2 2p^2$; the ground term is not immediately obvious. Ignoring the closed shells, the quantum numbers are

$$n_1 = 2 \qquad l_1 = 1$$

$$n_2 = 2 \qquad l_2 = 1$$

Pauli's Exclusion Principle requires that no two electrons have all four quantum numbers equal; simply by changing the values of m_l in the range of $+1, 0, -1$ and m_s having the value $\pm 1/2$ there are nine different possibilities if the electrons are assumed to be indistinguishable. It is easy to see which of these nine comprise the lowest energy state of the atom by using the familiar box diagram, with the difference that the compartments are not p_x, p_y, and p_z but $m_l = \pm 1, 0$. That is, for $l = 1$, $m_l = \pm 1, 0$, since $m_l = l, l - 1, \ldots -l$.

$$m_l = \quad +1 \qquad 0 \qquad -1$$

Hund's first rule now requires that as many electrons as possible have parallel spins in the lowest energy term. Hund's second rule requires that of all the possible terms of this type (i.e., having a maximum spin multiplicity), the one having the highest L value will be lowest in energy. Thus, the assignments having the largest possible M_L values must be found, since these must be associated with the term of highest L value. Taking account of Hund's first rule, there are only three possibilities:

However, the following assignment

for example, with $M_L = 2$ is not allowable since the spins are opposed, etc. These three "assignments," in fact, all have the same energy in the absence of a magnetic field (since m_l is not then defined!) and so they must all be components of a ^3P term. (^{3}, called "triplet," because $S = +1/2 + 1/2 = 1$ and $r = 2S + 1$ and $M_L = 1 + 0$, $1 - 1$, and $0 - 1$, i.e., $1, 0, -1$. Therefore, L must be unity, i.e., a P term). The other possible ways of assigning electrons to the "boxes" yield ^1S and ^1D terms, but they are "excited" terms, as Hund's rule clearly states. The reason why ^3P is lowest is quite clear from the box diagrams, since the electrons are always in different boxes, or orbitals, for this term, whereas for ^1D and ^1S they must, sometimes at least, be in the same orbital. That is, for the ^1D term, M_L must have the values $2, 1, 0, -1, -2$, and those for 2 and 0 are assigned as

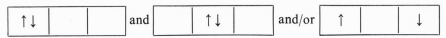

respectively, and the interelectronic repulsion energy is lower in the ^3P case. Thus it is said that interelectronic repulsion removes some of the degeneracy of the previously ninefold degenerate level (3×3 orbitally, since each p orbital has three equivalent lobes p_x, p_y, p_z, or $p_0, p_{\pm 1}$) and diagramatically the situation can be represented as in Fig. 1.1. It is clear that there is a large upward shift of all the levels when the negatively charged nature of the electrons is considered, this being required to change the "atom" from C^{2+} to C since two "neutral" electrons would result in the "atom" being positively charged (ignoring the closed shells). It is also necessary to remember that the somewhat more familiar p_x, p_y, and p_z orbitals are simply linear combinations of the $p_0, p_{\pm 1}$ "orbitals" used here, but the latter are to be preferred because ambiguities arise in the use of the x, y, z set if great care is not used. In fact, the correspondence can be defined as follows (3) and the notation in the last column will be used in discussing the angular parts of the atomic wavefunctions.

$$p_z = p_0 \qquad\qquad\qquad \equiv \langle 0|$$

$$p_x \equiv \frac{1}{\sqrt{2}}[p_{+1} + p_{-1}] \equiv \frac{1}{\sqrt{2}}[\langle 1| + \langle \bar{1}|]$$

$$p_y = \frac{-i}{\sqrt{2}}[p_{+1} - p_{-1}] \equiv \frac{-i}{\sqrt{2}}[\langle 1| - \langle \bar{1}|]$$

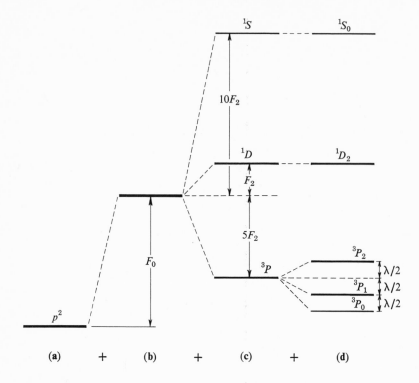

FIGURE 1.1.
   (a) no interelectronic repulsion
   (b) angular independent part of electron repulsion
   (c) angular dependent parts of electron repulsion: L and S now defined
   (d) inclusion of spin-orbit coupling: J now defined

This matter has been stressed because it is often more convenient to work mathematically with the $p_0, p_{\pm 1}$ functions rather than the p_x, p_y, p_z set.

The same comments apply to considerations of d orbital configurations and terms and (3)

$$d_{z^2} \equiv d_0 \qquad\qquad \equiv \langle 0|$$

$$d_{xz} = \frac{1}{\sqrt{2}}[d_{+1} + d_{-1}] \equiv \frac{1}{\sqrt{2}}[\langle 1| + \langle \bar{1}|]$$

$$d_{yz} = \frac{-i}{\sqrt{2}}[d_{+1} - d_{-1}] \equiv \frac{-i}{\sqrt{2}}[\langle 1| - \langle \bar{1}|]$$

$$d_{x^2-y^2} = \frac{1}{\sqrt{2}}[d_{+2} + d_{-2}] \equiv \frac{1}{\sqrt{2}}[\langle 2| + \langle \bar{2}|]$$

$$d_{xy} = \frac{-i}{\sqrt{2}} [d_{+2} - d_{-2}] \equiv \frac{-i}{\sqrt{2}} [\langle 2| - \langle \bar{2}|]$$

The use of the box-assignment method quickly shows that for an ion such as V^{2+}, with the configuration $\ldots 3s^2 3p^6 3d^2$, the lowest term is ^3F (triplet, since the spins must be parallel for lowest energy, and an F term since, for an assignment with parallel spins, the following have the largest $|M_L|$ values

2	1	0	−1	−2	
↑	↑				$M_L = +3$

2	1	0	−1	−2	
			↑	↑	$M_L = -3$

and so these must belong to a level with $L = 3$).

With a little experience in picking out the sets of M_L assignments it is easy to show that the configuration d^2 gives the terms ^3F, ^3P, ^1G, ^1D, ^1S, but it must be remembered that Hund's rules are only correct for the *lowest* possible level and do not say anything about the relative positions of the four higher terms; even though the ^1S term is always highest, the ^1D is usually lower than ^1G, and even lower than ^3P, so that experimental evidence must be taken into account at this stage of refinement. The importance of the order of the levels will be seen when the crystal field model is discussed.

(ii) Atomic Spectra

At the same level of sophistication of atomic structure as was discussed above it is possible to examine the conditions required for a transition between two energy states of an atom in which electric dipole radiation is either absorbed or emitted. It can be shown that

$$\Delta S = 0 \quad \text{and} \quad \Delta L = 0, \pm 1$$

and that, in addition, transitions are forbidden between terms arising from configurations of the same parity (parity being the property of "oddness" or "evenness" of the wavefunction when it is inverted through the nucleus, i.e., s orbitals are "even" or "g," and p orbitals are odd or "u"); in particular, transitions are forbidden between terms arising from the same configuration. This is known as Laporte's Rule and stems from the fact that if the initial and final states have wavefunctions of the same parity, it is not possible for "odd" parity electric dipole radiation to be absorbed or emitted by one of them in going to the other. Provided the coupling between the l_i is not too strong, the selection rule $\Delta L = 0, \pm 1$ becomes simply $\Delta l = \pm 1$; i.e., $s \leftrightarrow p \leftrightarrow d \leftrightarrow f$ but $s \nleftrightarrow d \nleftrightarrow g$, $p \nleftrightarrow f$, etc., and it is within this framework that it is possible to discuss the excitation of *an s* electron to a *p* orbital, and so on.

In the d^2 case, electric dipole transitions are forbidden between any two of the five terms arising from the configuration simply by Laporte's Rule. Thus, in atomic spectra, electric dipole transitions are at least restricted to terms arising from different configurations, and are even forbidden for these if they have the same overall parties.

This selection rule does not apply for electric quadrupole or magnetic dipole radiation, and even though the former are $\sim 10^{-8} - 10^{-12}$ times as strong as the electric dipole ones, yet they are known and must be born in mind. For such a transition $\Delta S = 0$, $\Delta L = 0$, ± 2 (quadrupole).

In fact, the levels denoted by term symbols are not single, being themselves split to a small extent for elements of low atomic number and more appreciably for the heavier elements. This results from the interaction of the orbital and spin angular momenta (since they both generate magnetic moments and these " couple " with each other in the electric field of the nucleus). Thus the inner quantum number *j* is defined such that, for a single electron

$$j = l + s, l + s - 1, \ldots l - s$$

or for an atom

$$J = L + S, L + S - 1 \ldots L - S$$

In the example of the carbon atom the ^3P term is more fully denoted by ^rL_J, where $J = 2, 1, 0$. That is, $^3P_2$, $^3P_1$, and $^3P_0$, these three *components* making up the *triplet P* term. Electric dipole transitions arise and terminate upon a single component of a term with the selection rules $\Delta J = 0$, ± 1. (There are no longer individual selection rules for ΔS and ΔL, since these are no longer " good " quantum numbers. Laporte's Rule still holds, however, since this concerns the overall symmetries of the combining levels and is unaltered by coupling changes.)

It is perhaps relatively easy to see, in the light of these selection rules, why visible color in solutions of Ti^{3+} ion seemed difficult to explain, since Ti^{3+} has the configuration … $3d^1$, i.e., ^2D term and the lowest excited term, ^2S, arises from the configuration … $4s^1$. For Russell-Saunders selection rules $\Delta L = \pm 1$, $\Delta S = 0$, the transition is forbidden for electric dipole radiation and, on taking into account the $L-S$ coupling, $J = 5/2$ and $3/2$ for the ^2D term and $J = 1/2$ for ^2S (since $L = 0$). Such transitions require $\Delta J = 2$ and $\Delta J = 1$ respectively so the first transition, at least, is forbidden for electric dipole radiation. In addition, both the ^2D and ^2S terms have even parity so that the transitions are electric dipole forbidden, even the $^2D_{3/2} \leftarrow {}^2S_{1/2}$. In the gaseous ion (*6*) there is a weak transition at $80,378$ cm^{-1}, which could be this transition provided the radiation observed is electric quadrupole or magnetic dipole; but, in any event, it seemed impossible to assign the transition in aqueous Ti^{3+} solutions (*7*) at $21,000$ *cm*$^{-1}$ to the Ti^{3+} ion by itself.

(iii) Hydrogenlike Wavefunctions

In deriving the selection rules stated above, it is necessary to assume certain forms for the one-electron wavefunctions and this also becomes necessary when the effects of "crystal fields" are considered in the next section. The one-electron hydrogenlike functions (3) are used, i.e.,

$$\Psi_{nlm} = R_{nl}(r)\Theta_{lm}(\theta)\Phi_m(\varphi)$$
$$= R_{nl}(r)Y_l^m(\theta, \varphi) \qquad \text{where } m = m_l$$

where the $Y_l^m(\theta\varphi)$ are spherical harmonics and the $R_{nl}(r)$ is the radial (or r dependent) part of the wavefunction which, in the treatment discussed here, will never be substituted for explicitly, but rather parametrically. The spherical harmonics are composed of the $\Theta_{lm}(\theta)$ part, which are simply associated Legendre polynomials normalized to unity, i.e.,

$$\Theta_{00} = \frac{1}{\sqrt{2}} \qquad \Theta_{10} = \sqrt{\frac{3}{2}}\cos\theta \qquad \Theta_{20} = \sqrt{\frac{5}{8}}(3\cos^2\theta - 1)$$

$$\Theta_{1\pm1} = \sqrt{\frac{3}{4}}\sin\theta \qquad \Theta_{2\pm1} = \sqrt{\frac{15}{4}}\sin\theta\cos\theta$$

$$\Theta_{2\pm2} = \sqrt{\frac{15}{16}}\sin^2\theta$$

By "normalized to unity" it is meant that

$$\int_0^\pi \Theta_{lm}{}^*\Theta_{l'm'}\sin\theta\,d\theta = \delta_{ll'}\delta_{mm'}$$
$$= 1 \text{ if } l' = l \quad \text{and} \quad m' = m$$
$$= 0 \text{ otherwise}$$

and the $\Phi_m(\varphi)$ are of the form

$$\Phi_0 = \frac{1}{\sqrt{2\pi}} \qquad \text{and} \qquad \Phi_{\pm m} = e^{\pm im\varphi}$$

and are also normalized to unity, i.e.,

$$\int_0^{2\pi} \Phi_m{}^*\Phi_{m'}\,d\varphi = \delta_{mm'}$$

and

$$\delta_{mm'} = 1 \text{ if } m = m'$$
$$= 0 \text{ otherwise}$$

Thus, integrals of the form

$$\int \Psi^* \Psi \, d\tau$$

are zero unless *both* the Θ and Φ parts of the integral are non-zero. Since φ is simply a cyclic coordinate, the probability densities do not depend upon it and the densities can be plotted diagramatically (or else simply the Θ part of the wavefunction) and these yield the familiar polar graphs (*4*) shown in Figs. 1.2 and 1.3.

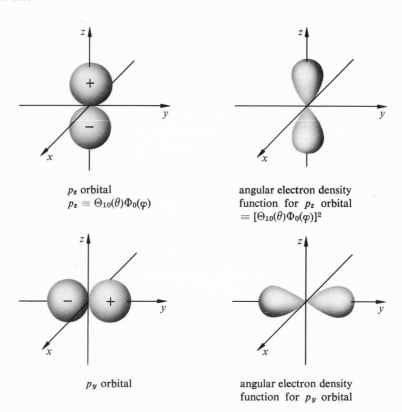

p_z orbital
$p_z \equiv \Theta_{10}(\theta)\Phi_0(\varphi)$

angular electron density
function for p_z orbital
$\equiv [\Theta_{10}(\theta)\Phi_0(\varphi)]^2$

p_y orbital

angular electron density
function for p_y orbital

FIGURE 1.2.

The interpretation of these graphs is of some importance and is easiest to follow for the p_z function, i.e., $p_0 \equiv \Theta_{10} \equiv \sqrt{3/2}\cos\theta$. The plot of $r = \cos\theta$ is simply two *spherical* lobes of opposite sign, whereas the plot of $r = \cos^2\theta$ is a solid of revolution of a lemniscate and has no sign attached to the lobes. It should be noted with regard to the p_x, p_y, d_{xy}, d_{xz}, etc., diagrams that these are linear combinations of the more fundamental $\langle m_l|$ functions. It should also be noted that the probability of finding an electron in the p orbital set is exactly the same whether the direction is along x, y, z or the 111 axis. (Equally, it is not obvious whether the approach to a set of orbitals d_{xy}, d_{xz}, d_{yz} along the 111 axis is along a path of low electron density or not, and it will be shown later that this is *not* the line of minimum probability for this set!)

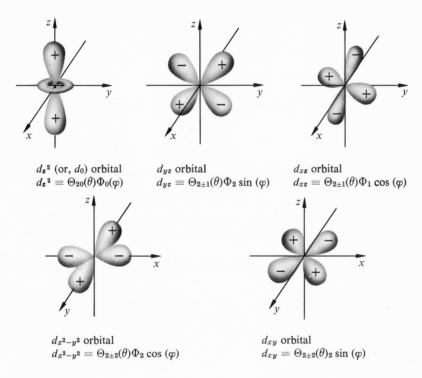

d_{z^2} (or, d_0) orbital
$d_{z^2} \equiv \Theta_{20}(\theta)\Phi_0(\varphi)$

d_{yz} orbital
$d_{yz} \equiv \Theta_{2\pm1}(\theta)\Phi_2 \sin(\varphi)$

d_{xz} orbital
$d_{xz} \equiv \Theta_{2\pm1}(\theta)\Phi_1 \cos(\varphi)$

$d_{x^2-y^2}$ orbital
$d_{x^2-y^2} \equiv \Theta_{2\pm2}(\theta)\Phi_2 \cos(\varphi)$

d_{xy} orbital
$d_{xy} \equiv \Theta_{2\pm2}(\theta)_2 \sin(\varphi)$

FIGURE 1.3.

B. THE CRYSTAL FIELD APPROXIMATION (8–16)

In this approximation, the nearest neighbor (or coordinated) atoms closest to the "central" paramagnetic transition metal ion are assumed to act simply as sources of negative charge and the effect of these charges on the central ion energy levels is calculated. In the simplest approach (9) the positive and negative ions are assumed to be hard nonoverlapping spheres in contact with each other so that they can be represented as point charges at either the several nuclei or else at some "effective" internuclear distance from the central ion.

Since the d electrons are situated on the central metal ion, it is convenient to relate the electrostatic potential of the assembly of negative charges to a set of coordinates centered on the transition metal ion. In the particular case of an octahedral set of charges it is convenient to imagine the central ion as the origin of a set of cartesian axes and polar coordinates, the negative charges of magnitude Ze being at a distance $\pm a$ along the x, y, and z axes and the polar angles θ and φ being measured from the $+z$ axis and $+x$ axis as references (see Fig. 1.4).

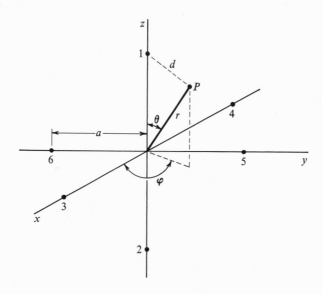

FIGURE 1.4.

(i) Expansion of the Field Potential (Octahedral)

It is desired then, to determine the potential of the six negative charges at some general point P in terms of the coordinate set centered on the transition metal ion. This standard problem in classical electrostatics is briefly outlined below. If the charges are numbered 1/.../6 in the order shown in the figure, then the potential at P due to charge number 1, V_1, is given by

$$V_1 = + \frac{Ze^2}{d}$$

d being the distance from charge 1 to P.
Now

$$d = \sqrt{a^2 + r^2 - 2ar \cos \theta} = a\sqrt{1 + (r/a)^2 - 2(r/a)\cos \theta}$$

and the reciprocal of expressions of this type can be expanded in terms of Legendre polynomials (3). In particular, the simplification is made that $r < a$, so that the (small) portion of the d electron outside the sphere of radius "a" is ignored. It can be shown that

$$\frac{1}{\sqrt{1 - 2qt + q^2}} = \sum_{l=0}^{\infty} P_l(t)q^l$$

where

$$P_l(t) = \frac{1}{2^l l!} \frac{d^l}{dt^l} (t^2 - 1)^l$$

that is,

$$V_1 = \frac{Ze^2}{a} \sum_{l=0}^{\infty} \left(\frac{r}{a}\right)^l P_l(\cos \theta)$$

and

$$P_0(\cos \theta) = 1$$

$$P_1(\cos \theta) = \cos \theta$$

$$P_2(\cos \theta) = (3 \cos^2 \theta - 1)$$

$$P_3(\cos \theta) = \tfrac{1}{2}(5 \cos^3 \theta - 3 \cos \theta)$$

$$P_4(\cos \theta) = \tfrac{1}{8}(35 \cos^4 \theta - 30 \cos^2 \theta + 3)$$

Terms with $l > 4$ are not necessary, since their contribution will be zero for d electrons.
Thus

$$V_1 = \frac{Ze^2}{a} \left[1 + \left(\frac{r}{a}\right) P_1(\cos \theta) + \left(\frac{r}{a}\right)^2 P_2(\cos \theta) \right.$$
$$\left. + \left(\frac{r}{a}\right)^3 P_3(\cos \theta) + \left(\frac{r}{a}\right)^4 P_4(\cos \theta) \right]$$

and since $\cos^n(\theta + \pi) = -\cos^n \theta$ for n odd, then

$$V_1 + V_2 = \frac{Ze^2}{a} \left[1 + \left(\frac{r}{a}\right)^2 P_2(\cos \theta) + \left(\frac{r}{a}\right)^4 P_4(\cos \theta) \right]$$

Substituting for $P_l(\cos \theta)$ and putting $\cos \theta = z/r$ yields

$$V_1 + V_2 = \frac{Ze^2}{a} \left[1 + \tfrac{1}{2}\left(\frac{r}{a}\right)\left(\frac{3z^2}{r^2} - 1\right) + \tfrac{1}{8}\left(\frac{r}{a}\right)^4\left(\frac{35z^4}{r^4} - \frac{30z^2}{r^2} + 3\right) \right]$$

Similarly,

$$V_3 + V_4 = \frac{Ze^2}{a} \left[1 + \tfrac{1}{2}\left(\frac{r}{a}\right)\left(\frac{3x^2}{r^2} - 1\right) + \tfrac{1}{8}\left(\frac{r}{a}\right)^4\left(\frac{35x^4}{r^4} - \frac{30x^2}{r^2} + 3\right) \right]$$

and the same for $V_5 + V_6$, with y in place of x.

$$\therefore \quad V = \sum_{i=1}^{6} V_i = 6\,\frac{Ze^2}{a} + \frac{35Ze^2}{4a^5}\,(x^4 + y^4 + z^4 - \tfrac{3}{5}r^4)$$

$$= 6\,\frac{Ze^2}{a} + D(x^4 + y^4 + z^4 - \tfrac{3}{5}r^4) \qquad \text{where } D = \frac{35Ze^2}{4a^5}$$

The same problem can be expressed in terms of spherical harmonics (12), Y_l^m, when

$$V = \frac{7Ze}{3a^5}\,\pi^{\frac{1}{2}}r^4[Y_4^{\,0} + (5/14)^{\frac{1}{2}}(Y_4^{\,4} + Y_4^{\,-4})]$$

its being remembered that the choice of polar (z) axis is not arbitrary but is as defined in Fig. 1.2].

(ii) Calculation of the Matrix Elements for d^1

The form of the potential perturbing the central ion d electron has now been established, and perturbation theory gives the first-order perturbation energy as

$$\int \Psi^* V \Psi \, d\tau \equiv \langle \Psi | V | \Psi \rangle$$

where Ψ is the atomic wavefunction of the ^2D term of the atom. Alternatively, it is possible to "replace" Ψ by the one electron wavefunction for a d electron ϕ_m which is, of course, the same thing when it is recalled that there are five equally valid orbital wavefunctions that can be used. Thus, the energy level is fivefold degenerate corresponding in the first case to the five values of M_L and in the second place to the five values of m_l (which are identical to M_L in this case and have values 2, 1, 0, -1, -2).

It is necessary, therefore, to apply the methods of perturbation theory of degenerate systems (3) and to calculate the quantities $\langle m_l | V | m_l' \rangle \equiv \langle M_L | V | M_L' \rangle$. The d orbitals all have the same radial wavefunction so that this will be treated the same for all the wavefunctions, i.e., it is possible to write

$$\int_0^{\infty}\int_0^{\pi}\int_0^{2\pi} R_{nl}(r)\Theta_{lm}(\theta)\Phi_m(\varphi)VR_{nl'}(r)\Theta_{l'm'}(\theta)\Phi_{m'}(\varphi)r^2 \sin\theta \, dr \, d\theta \, d\varphi$$

$$\equiv \int_0^{\infty} R_{nl}(r)V(r)R_{nl'}(r)r^2 \, dr \int_0^{\pi}\int_0^{2\pi} \Theta_{lm}(\theta)\Phi_m(\varphi)V(\theta,\varphi)\Theta_{l'm'}(\theta)\Phi_{m'} \sin\theta \, d\theta \, d\varphi$$

$$= \langle R_{nl} | V(r) | R_{nl'} \rangle \langle lm | V(\theta,\varphi) | l'm' \rangle.$$

where m_l has been written simply as m to avoid complex notation, and in future the l will not be indicated since all the electrons have $l = 2 = l'$.

The integral involving the radial part of the wavefunction is not usually solved but, instead, is substituted parametrically; the θ and φ dependent part can be reduced to simple numbers, as will be seen below. Thus it is mainly required to determine the values of the 25 quantities

$$\langle m|D(x^4 + y^4 + z^4)|m'\rangle$$

The term $6\,Ze^2/a$ is clearly spherically symmetrical and cannot cause any splitting of levels. All it does is to raise the whole set of d orbital energies by the same amount $(6Ze^2/a)$. This corresponds to the same sort of thing as the inclusion of the negative character of the electron in the case of the carbon atom, since, the net charge on the ion cluster is no longer positive (if $Z = 1$ then the cluster is net $4-$) and the ionization potential of the d electron is clearly changed by a large amount. It must be emphasized that the magnitude of the splitting because of the last term in the perturbation potential will always be a very small one compared to the shift in the whole set of energies (using the point charge model). It is equally possible to represent the nearest neighbor atoms, ions, or molecules by negative pole inward dipoles. If these are used, the shift term will be much smaller than for a point charge model; however, *most* of the results which the crystal field approximation yields do not depend upon the size of this shift so it will not be considered further in this section.

The reduction of the quantities $\langle m|D(x^4 + y^4 + z^4)|m'\rangle$ is carried out in two stages; then the final substitution of parameters for the radial part is done, and finally the secular determinant for the perturbation energy is solved in terms of the parameters. The term $-3/5\ r^4$ is dealt with last of all in the r dependent part.

(a) The φ dependent part of the integrals

$$x^4 + y^4 = r^4 \sin^4 \theta(\sin^4 \varphi + \cos^4 \varphi) \quad \text{and} \quad z \text{ is } \varphi \text{ independent.}$$

The d electron wavefunctions are all of the form

$$\Psi_{nlm} = R_{nl}(r)\Theta_{lm}(\theta)\Phi_m(\varphi)$$

where $\Phi_m(\varphi)$ is as defined above, so that the value of integrals of the type

$$\int_0^{2\pi} e^{im\varphi}(\sin^4 \varphi + \cos^4 \varphi)e^{-im'\varphi}\,d\varphi \text{ is required} \equiv \langle \Phi(m)|\sin^4 \varphi + \cos^4 \varphi|\Phi(m')\rangle$$

$$(\sin^4 \varphi + \cos^4 \varphi) = \left(\frac{e^{i\varphi} - e^{-i\varphi}}{2i}\right)^4 + \left(\frac{e^{i\varphi} + e^{-i\varphi}}{2}\right)^4$$

$$= \frac{e^{4i\varphi} + e^{-4i\varphi} + 6}{8}$$

i.e., the values of the integrals

$$\tfrac{1}{8}\int e^{im\varphi}(e^{4i\varphi} + e^{-4i\varphi} + 6)e^{-im'\varphi}\,d\varphi \text{ are required}$$

and these are zero unless either

$$m = m' \pm 4 \quad \text{when} \quad \langle \Phi(m) | x^4 + y^4 | \Phi(m') \rangle = \tfrac{1}{8} r^4 \sin^4 \theta$$

or

$$m = m \qquad \text{when} \quad \langle \Phi(m) | x^4 + y^4 | \Phi(m') \rangle = \tfrac{3}{4} r^4 \sin^4 \theta$$

Thus the perturbation secular determinant has already been reduced to seven elements

$$
\begin{array}{c|ccccc}
m_l & 2 & 1 & 0 & \bar{1} & \bar{2} \\
\hline
2 & x & & & & x \\
1 & & x & & & \\
0 & & & x & & \\
\bar{1} & & & & x & \\
\bar{2} & x & & & & x \\
\end{array}
$$

where x denotes non-zero elements (not necessarily equal).

(b) Solution of the θ integrals

As an example consider

$$\int_0^\pi \Theta_{20} \langle \Phi(m) | x^4 + y^4 + z^4 | \Phi(m') \rangle \Theta_{20} \sin \theta \, d\theta$$

Substituting for

$$\langle \Phi(m) | (x^4 + y^4 + z^4) | \Phi(m') \rangle = r^4 (\tfrac{3}{4} \sin^4 \theta + \cos^4 \theta)$$

(since $m' = m$ and $z = r \cos \theta$)

$$r^4 \langle \Theta_{20} | (\tfrac{3}{4} \sin^4 \theta + \cos^4 \theta) | \Theta_{20} \rangle$$

$$= \tfrac{5}{8} r^4 \int_0^\pi (3 \cos^2 \theta - 1)^2 (\tfrac{3}{4} \sin^4 \theta + \cos^4 \theta) \sin \theta \, d\theta$$

$$\therefore \quad \langle 0 | (x^4 + y^4 + z^4) | 0 \rangle = \tfrac{5}{4} r^4 \left[\frac{27}{4} \int_0^{\pi/2} \cos^4 \theta \sin^5 \theta \, d\theta - \frac{9}{2} \int_0^{\pi/2} \cos^2 \theta \sin^5 \theta \, d\theta \right.$$

$$+ \tfrac{3}{4} \int_0^{\pi/2} \sin^5 \theta \, d\theta + 9 \int_0^{\pi/2} \cos^8 \theta \sin \theta \, d\theta$$

$$\left. - 6 \int_0^{\pi/2} \cos^6 \theta \sin \theta \, d\theta + \int_0^{\pi/2} \cos^4 \theta \sin \theta \, d\theta \right]$$

and the integrals are now standard forms (3) and refine as follows

$$= \frac{5}{4} r^4 \left[\frac{27}{4} \cdot \frac{8 \cdot 3}{3 \cdot 5 \cdot 7 \cdot 9} - \frac{9}{2} \cdot \frac{8}{3 \cdot 5 \cdot 7} + \frac{3}{4} \cdot \frac{8}{3 \cdot 5} + \frac{9}{9} - \frac{6}{7} + \frac{1}{5} \right]$$

$$= \left(\frac{5}{4} \times \frac{20}{35} \right) r^4 = \tfrac{5}{7} r^4$$

The other θ dependent integrals can be similarly evaluated, all seven being non-zero and

$$\langle 0|(x^4 + y^4 + z^4)|0\rangle = \tfrac{5}{7}r^4$$

$$\langle 1|(x^4 + y^4 + z^4)|1\rangle \equiv \langle \bar{1}|(x^4 + y^4 + z^4)|\bar{1}\rangle = 11/21 \ r^4$$

$$\langle 2|(x^4 + y^4 + z^4)|2\rangle \equiv \langle \bar{2}|(x^4 + y^4 + z^4)|\bar{2}\rangle = 13/21 \ r^4$$

$$\langle 2| \ x^4 + y^4 + z^4 \ |\bar{2}\rangle \equiv \langle \bar{2}| \ x^4 + y^4 + z^4 \ |2\rangle = 73/105 \ r^4$$

(c) Simplification of the radial part and solution of the secular determinant

The complete solution of the radial part of the perturbation energy is not possible because the orbitals are not completely hydrogenlike, nor are the Slater functions much of an improvement without a great deal of additional refinement. Instead, the integral

$$\int_0^\infty R_{nl}{}^2(r)r^4r^2 \ dr$$

is replaced by a parameter. Thus, for example,

$$\langle \psi(0)|V|\psi(0)\rangle \equiv \langle \psi(0)|D(x^4 + y^4 + z^4 - \tfrac{3}{5}r^4)|\psi(0)\rangle$$

$$= \tfrac{5}{7}D \int_0^\infty R_{nl}{}^2r^4r^2 \ dr - \tfrac{3}{5}D \int_0^\infty R_{nl}{}^2r^4r^2 \ dr$$

$$= \frac{12}{105} D \int_0^\infty R_{nl}{}^2r^4r^2 \ dr$$

$$= 6Dq \qquad \text{where } q = \frac{2}{105}\int_0^\infty R_{nl}{}^2r^4r^2 \ dr = \frac{2}{105}\overline{r^4}$$

and where $\psi(M_L)$ is used to denote the particular component of the fivefold degenerate wavefunction which, in this one electron example, is identical with ϕ_m (see the 2 electron example below, however).

Similarly, $\langle \psi(1)|V|\psi(1)\rangle \equiv \langle \psi(\bar{1})|V|\psi(\bar{1})\rangle = -4Dq$

$$\langle \psi(2)|V|\psi(2)\rangle \equiv \langle \psi(\bar{2})|V|\psi(\bar{2})\rangle = Dq$$

$$\langle \psi(\bar{2})|V|\psi(2)\rangle \equiv \langle \psi(2)|V|\psi(\bar{2})\rangle = 5Dq$$

so that the perturbation secular determinant for the energy becomes

$$\begin{vmatrix} Dq - E & 0 & 0 & 0 & 5Dq \\ 0 & -4Dq - E & 0 & 0 & 0 \\ 0 & 0 & 6Dq - E & 0 & 0 \\ 0 & 0 & 0 & -4Dq - E & 0 \\ 5Dq & 0 & 0 & 0 & Dq - E \end{vmatrix} = 0$$

and the roots are $E = -4Dq$ (thrice), $+6Dq$ (twice), i.e., the previously fivefold degenerate D term has been split into two new levels, the lower of which is threefold degenerate and the upper of which is doubly degenerate (Dq is a positive parameter, as inspection shows).

It is now possible to substitute back the energies of the two levels into the secular equations and to obtain wavefunctions for the perturbed atom. These turn out to be the well-known d_{xz}, d_{yz}, d_{xy} set for the triply degenerate level and $d_{x^2-y^2}$ and d_{z^2} for the doubly degenerate level. Since the latter set points directly toward the negative charges, whereas the former has the angular maxima between the charges, it becomes possible to visualize physically that a single d electron in the original set of five orbitals will favor occupation of the d_{xy}, d_{yz}, d_{xz} set, since these avoid the regions of largest repulsive potential (i.e., their energy is lower).

(iii) Energy-Level Diagrams for d^1

The final result can thus be depicted either as the splitting of the fivefold degenerate d orbital set to give a low-lying set of three orbitals and a higher pair of two (discussed above) as shown in Fig. 1.5, or else as a splitting of a ^2D term

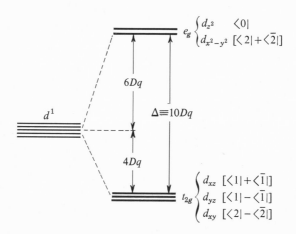

FIGURE 1.5.

(to give a $^2T_{2g}$ term and a ^2E_g term using the group theoretical notation pertinant to the octahedral group O_h) as in Fig. 1.6.

As is clear from the figures, the splitting interval is 10 Dq, sometimes written Δ, and the color of simple d^1 complexes such as $[Ti(H_2O)_6]^{3+}$ in the visible is due to a transition which is represented configurationally as $e_g \leftarrow t_{2g}$ or, on a term basis, as $^2E_g \leftarrow ^2T_{2g}$. This assignment was first made by Ilse and Hartmann in 1951 (7) and its essential correctness has been borne out by subsequent work.

As the transition stands, it is clearly Laporte forbidden, since both the ground and excited states have the same parity (g) and such a transition should occur only as an electric quadrupole, or magnetic dipole, emission or absorption. However, it has been conclusively shown by Carlin and Piper (*17*) that the intensity is predominantly of the electric dipole type and the only way in which this can happen is if the molecular center of symmetry is removed by a vibration which is "u" in parity. The transition is then said to be "vibronically" allowed, since the upper and lower vibronic states (vibration × electronic) will have opposite parities. This aspect of crystal field theory will not be discussed further here, since there are adequate references in other texts and papers.

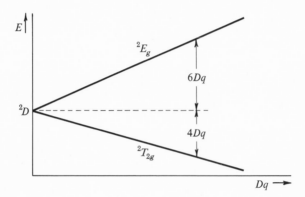

FIGURE 1.6.

In the complex $[Ti(H_2O)_6]^{3+}$, the absorption has a maximum at about 20,300 cm^{-1} so that $\Delta(\equiv 10\ Dq)$ is of this magnitude for the tripositive ions of the first transition series and investigation of the first row dipositive ions shows that the value is about $10,000 - 12,000$ cm^{-1} for them (*18, 19, 20*). The splitting has many consequences—spectroscopic, magnetic, and thermodynamic—and it is with the broad aspects of these consequences that this series is concerned.

Only the one-electron case has been discussed as yet, and the two- and poly-electronic cases must now be briefly outlined. Before this is done, however, it is necessary to point out that the d^9 configuration also has only a ^2D term and the calculation of the splitting will proceed exactly as for the d^1 case except in one feature. This is that d^9 is like a full shell, d^{10}, minus an electron, and this "hole" can be treated as though it were a single electron of opposite charge. Thus, instead of going into the t_{2g} subshell it will go into the e_g and the whole pattern of levels for the hole is thus in the reverse order to that for d^1. The same thing occurs for both d^4 and d^6, since in these cases the half-filled d^5 shell has an A_{1g} ground term and one less or one more electron can be treated as a one-electron problem. Clearly, the d^4 will behave like d^9 and the d^6 like d^1; the final diagram of energy: Dq (Orgel diagram), is as shown in Fig. 1.7.

This leaves only d^2, d^3, d^5, d^7, and d^8 to be discussed, and the pairs d^2, d^7 and d^3, d^8 are related in the same way as $d^1 d^6$ and $d^4 d^9$, so that, essentially, only d^2 and d^5 have to be worked in detail.

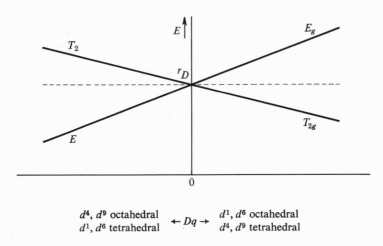

$$
\begin{array}{ccc}
d^4, d^9 \text{ octahedral} & & d^1, d^6 \text{ octahedral} \\
d^1, d^6 \text{ tetrahedral} & \leftarrow Dq \rightarrow & d^4, d^9 \text{ tetrahedral}
\end{array}
$$

FIGURE 1.7.

(iv) The Two-Electron Problem

The starting point is to set up the seven orthogonal orbital wavefunctions which belong to the atomic F term (*21*) (since it has been shown that the ground term of a d^2 atom or ion is ^3F and that there is another term of triplet multiplicity not too far in energy away, ^3P). These seven functions are the seven which have different values of M_L, i.e., $\psi(3), \psi(2), \psi(1) \dots \psi(\bar{3})$, and they can be written as simple product functions of the one-electron functions ϕ_m used previously for the d^1 calculations.

Thus

$$\psi_F(3) = \phi_2 \phi_1$$

$$\psi_F(2) = \phi_2 \phi_0$$

However, there are two ways of getting $\psi(1)$, i.e., $\phi_1 \phi_0$ and $\phi_2 \phi_{\bar{1}}$, and a linear combination of these must be found by the usual methods (*3, 21*). The correct function is

$$\psi_F(1) = (2/5)^{\frac{1}{2}} \phi_1 \phi_0 + (3/5)^{\frac{1}{2}} \phi_2 \phi_{\bar{1}}$$

For $\psi(0)$

$$\psi_F(0) = (1/5)^{\frac{1}{2}} \phi_1 \phi_{\bar{1}} - (4/5)^{\frac{1}{2}} \phi_2 \phi_{\bar{2}}$$

with similar expressons for the $\psi_F(\bar{1})$ and $\psi_P(1)$, $\psi_P(0)$ and $\psi_P(\bar{1})$ functions, the $\psi_P(i)$ functions being chosen orthogonal to the $\psi_F(i)$.

The potential of the crystalline field is now expanded as before, except that it now contains two terms $V = V_1 + V_2$ pertinent to the two electrons.

The 49 matrix elements $\langle\psi_F|V|\psi_F\rangle$ are then calculated, there being, finally, only 6 elements to actually calculate because of equalities such as

$$\langle\psi(M)|V|\psi(M)\rangle = \langle\psi(\bar{M})|V|\psi(\bar{M})\rangle,$$

and

$$\langle\psi(\bar{M})|V|\psi(N)\rangle = \langle\psi(M)|V|\psi(\bar{N})\rangle = \langle\psi(\bar{N})|V|\psi(M)\rangle = \langle\psi(N)|V|\psi(\bar{M})\rangle$$

When V is replaced by $V_1 + V_2$ and the individual $\psi(M)$ are replaced by products of the more primitive one-electron functions ϕ_m, the matrix elements break up into one-electron integrals whose θ and φ dependent parts have been already calculated and the radial parts are combined with the θ and φ contributions and expressed parametrically by q once again.

As an example consider

$$\langle\psi_F(3)|V|\psi_F(3)\rangle$$

$$\langle\psi_F(3)|V|\psi_F(3)\rangle = \langle\phi_2\phi_1|V_1 + V_2|\phi_2\phi_1\rangle$$

$$= \langle\phi_2|V_1|\phi_2\rangle + \langle\phi_1|V_2|\phi_1\rangle$$

$$= \qquad Dq \qquad - \qquad 4Dq$$

$$= -3Dq$$

Whence (dropping the ψ's)

$$\langle 3|V|3\rangle \equiv \langle\bar{3}|V|\bar{3}\rangle = -3Dq$$

$$\langle 2|V|2\rangle \equiv \langle\bar{2}|V|\bar{2}\rangle = 7Dq$$

$$\langle 1|V|1\rangle \equiv \langle\bar{1}|V|\bar{1}\rangle = -Dq$$

$$\langle 0|V|0\rangle \qquad\qquad = -6Dq$$

$$\langle 3|V|\bar{1}\rangle \equiv \langle\bar{3}|V|1\rangle = 15^{\ddagger}Dq$$

$$\langle 2|V|\bar{2}\rangle \equiv \langle\bar{2}|V|2\rangle = 5Dq$$

Thus the secular determinant for the energy becomes

$$
\begin{array}{c|ccccccc}
3 & x & . & . & . & x & . & . \\
2 & . & x & & & & x & . \\
1 & & & x & & & & x \\
0 & & & & x & & & \\
\bar{1} & x & & & & x & & \\
\bar{2} & & x & & & & x & \\
\bar{3} & & & x & & & & x \\
\end{array} = 0
$$

where the x's denote non-zero entries of the type $pDq - SE$ (S being the over-lap $\equiv 0$ unless $M = M'$) and the p's being given above.

This determinant can be reduced to four *independent* determinants, of which two are identical:

$$\begin{vmatrix} -3Dq - E & 15^{\frac{1}{2}}Dq \\ 15^{\frac{1}{2}}Dq & -3Dq - E \end{vmatrix} = 0 \qquad \begin{vmatrix} 7Dq - E & 5Dq \\ 5Dq & 7Dq - E \end{vmatrix} = 0$$

$$\text{(I), (II)} \qquad\qquad\qquad\qquad \text{(III)}$$

$$|-6Dq - E| = 0$$

$$\text{(IV)}$$

and the roots are

$$-6Dq \text{ (thrice, from I, II, and IV)}$$

$$+2Dq \text{ (thrice, from I, II, and III)}$$

$$+12Dq \text{ (once, from III)}$$

The ^3F term is thus seen to split into three new levels, two of which are triply degenerate and the third of which is nondegenerate. By substituting back the energies in the secular equations it is possible to obtain the new wavefunctions

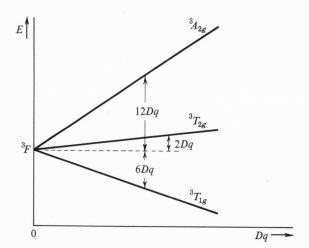

FIGURE 1.8.

for the perturbed problem and to show that these have symmetries T_{1g} for the lowest-lying orbital triplet $(-6Dq)$, T_{2g} at $+2Dq$ and A_{2g} at $+12Dq$. Thus the Orgel diagram for d^2 in an octahedral field takes the appearance shown in Fig. 1.8.

Nothing, as yet, has been said about what happens to the ^3P term, but it can be shown that the term remains orbitally threefold degenerate and is unsplit in the octahedral field. Its new symmetry is, however, T_{1g} and since terms of like symmetry can interact with one another, it is necessary to find out whether this does happen or not. To distinguish the origins of the two different $^3T_{1g}$ terms it is convenient to label them $T_{1g}(F)$ and $T_{1g}(P)$.

Thus the magnitude of $\langle \Psi[T_{1g}(F)] | V | \Psi[T_{1g}(P)] \rangle$ is required. Substituting the appropriate wavefunctions into this expression leads to a secular determinant.

$$\begin{vmatrix} -6Dq - E & 4Dq \\ 4Dq & X - E \end{vmatrix} = 0$$

where $-6Dq$ is the energy of the $^3T_{1g}(F)$ term and X is the (experimental or theoretical) height of the ^3P term of the field free atom or ion above ^3F. The matrix element between the two terms in the presence of the crystal field is $4Dq$.

It is not possible to give specific roots for such a determinant, since X is "unknown" and the magnitudes depend upon its value. The net effect is to depress

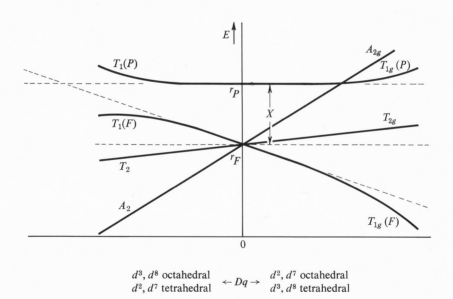

d^3, d^8 octahedral d^2, d^7 octahedral
d^2, d^7 tetrahedral $\leftarrow Dq \rightarrow$ d^3, d^8 tetrahedral

FIGURE 1.9.

the previous $^3T_{1g}(F)$ level and to raise the previous $^3T_{1g}(P)$ level by "mixing in" a little of each wavefunction with the other. The curves for these two levels thus become nonlinear with respect to Dq. Clearly, if $X = 0$, the ^3F and ^3P terms coincide and the determinant has roots $+2Dq$ and $-8Dq$ while for $X = \infty$ there is no interaction and the "root" is still $-6Dq$. The most that can happen, then, is that the $T_{1g}(F)$ level at $-6Dq$ can be depressed to $-8Dq$ and the $T_{1g}(P)$ level pushed up from 0 to $+2Dq$. In practice $X \sim 10,000 - 15,000 \text{ cm}^{-1}$ and the values will be intermediate between those given above.

All this leads to the diagram Fig. 1.9, it being important to notice that the diagram for d^3, d^8 is not obtained simply by extending the lines of the corresponding levels for d^2, d^7 because of the "noncrossing" rule and the nonlinearity of the T_{1g} levels with Dq. (The A_{2g} and T_{2g} levels will be perfectly linear and extensible.)

(v) Discussion of the Energy-Level Diagrams

Probably the most important single result is that the ground states of the d^2, d^7 configurations are orbital triplets whereas the ground states of d^3, d^8 configurations are orbitally single, i.e., nondegenerate orbitally. This is of the greatest importance from a magnetic standpoint, as will be seen later.

So far only levels having maximum spin multiplicity have been considered whereas, in V^{3+}, for example, there are three orbital singlets $^1G, ^1D$, and ^1S, while in Cr^{3+} there are six terms of spin multiplicity lower than four—$^2H, ^2G, ^2F, ^2D(2)$, and ^2P. A complete list of such levels can be found in any book on atomic spectra and will not be discussed here except to point out what terms arise from a few of these in an octahedral crystalline field (see Table 1.1).

TABLE 1.1.

	A_{1g}	A_{2g}	E_g	T_{1g}	T_{2g}
S	1				
P				1	
D			1		1
F		1		1	1
G	1		1	1	1
H	1	1	1	1	2

The inclusion of these lower multiplicity terms in the energy diagram will not be discussed here explicitly (8, 12, 13) but the methods and results can be found in various texts and published papers (22, 23, 24, 25).

The only configuration left to be discussed is d^5 and this is, in many ways, one of the most important from the point of view of correlating theoretical calculations with experimental results (11). The method for obtaining the energy-level diagram is much as outlined earlier for d^2, with two important differences: (1) there are *no* transitions which are "spin allowed," i.e., which have $\Delta S = 0$; and (2) there are no crystal field splittings of the atomic terms in the first-order approximation. The reasons for these differences are readily seen. The d^5 configuration of a free ion such as Mn^{2+}, Fe^{3+}, etc. has a ^6S term as its ground term. Using the box assignment method it is clear that there is only one way of having all five electrons with parallel spins, viz.

2	1	0	$\bar{1}$	$\bar{2}$
↑	↑	↑	↑	↑

and for this assignment $M_L = 0$, i.e., $L = 0$ and it must be a ^6S term (sextet, because $5 \times 1/2 \times 2 + 1 = 6$). There are no other sextet terms of this configuration (d^5) and all excited terms must be quartets or doublets. The box method shows that the quartet with the largest value of L is ^4G,

m_l	2	1	0	$\bar{1}$	$\bar{2}$
	↑↓	↑	↑	↑	

i.e., $M_L = 4 \therefore L = 4$; a G term and $S = 3 \times 1/2 \therefore r = 4$. It happens that this is also the lowest of the quartet terms. (Remember that Hund's rules do not necessarily hold for excited states). The other quartets may be shown (21) to be ^4F, ^4D, and ^4P. The doublets can be ignored, since the transitions (if any!) are bound to be weak, since $\Delta S = -1$ even for the sextet → quartet transition, let alone $\Delta S = -2$ for the sextet → doublet cases.

The possible configurations of the ground and excited states when the ion is in a cubic crystalline field are shown diagramatically in Fig. 1.10 and it can be

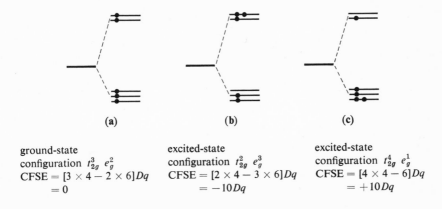

(a)	(b)	(c)
ground-state configuration $t_{2g}^3 e_g^2$	excited-state configuration $t_{2g}^2 e_g^3$	excited-state configuration $t_{2g}^4 e_g^1$
CFSE = $[3 \times 4 - 2 \times 6]Dq$	CFSE = $[2 \times 4 - 3 \times 6]Dq$	CFSE = $[4 \times 4 - 6]Dq$
= 0	= $-10Dq$	= $+10Dq$

FIGURE 1.10.

seen that the *net* crystal field stabilization energy is zero (as it is for for the ground term) and it turns out that this applies to all the individual terms and there is no first-order splitting.

However, just as the $^3T_{1g}(P)$ and $^3T_{1g}(F)$ terms interact in the presence of the field, so do the terms of the same type which arise from the individual atomic quartet terms. The splittings which do occur are the result, then, of second-order interactions of this type. Thus the matrix elements composing the perturbation secular determinants (*19, 25, 26*) are all of the type where the diagonal perturbation energies are zero and only nondiagonal terms contribute to the splitting.

The actual perturbation secular determinants will not be given here since they are available in many other places (*19, 25, 26*) and there are no new principles involved in them. The form of the Orgel diagram, shown in Fig. 1.11, will be discussed in more detail when the spectra are considered.

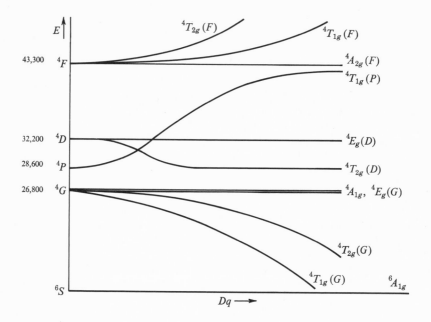

FIGURE 1.11.

All of the above derivation and discussion formally relates to an octahedrally disposed set of charges; however, the results are essentially the same for a tetrahedral array since both are subgroups of the cubic symmetry group. That this is so is easy to see since, if the 111 axis and the seven similar axes are considered as a set, then any set of eight charges placed on these axes at equal distances from the origin will simply be two interpenetrating tetrahedra. Qualitatively, the splitting pattern produced by such a set of charges will be exactly the same if only one of each pair (e.g., one of the pair on the 111 and $\bar{1}\bar{1}\bar{1}$ axes, respectively) is chosen and the other removed. (The same is true for the octahedron where it is possible to remove the charges along the $\bar{x}$, $\bar{y}$, and $\bar{z}$ axes without changing the level pattern, since the electrons being perturbed have a center of symmetry and, in the limit of no mixing with other states, the pattern produced by perturbing "half" of the lobes will be the same as that produced by perturbing "all" of the lobes.) The tetrahedral model is obtained by removing four of the eight charges, i.e., those from alternate vertices.

The main difference is, however, that whereas a single d electron in an octahedral charge array will be lower in the t_{2g} set of orbitals, in the tetrahedral array it will be lower in the e_g set, since these now point more or less in between the negative charges. Thus the pattern for d^1 (tetrahedral) is inverted with respect to d^1 (octahedral).

From a quantitative approach there is quite a difference, since in the first case there are six charges and in the latter, four. In addition, they (the four) are not as strategically situated and their effectiveness is reduced to 2/3 of their octahedral counterpart. Thus the tetrahedral splitting is inverted and $\sim 2/3 \times 2/3$, i.e., 4/9 of the octahedral on theoretical grounds. This shows that the same diagram as Fig. 1.7 can be used for tetrahedral complexes simply by switching the configuration (or by changing the sign of Dq), the octahedral d^1 and d^6 configurations having, qualitatively, the same pattern as d^4 and d^9 tetrahedral configurations. This justifies the lower line under Fig. 1.7. The argument for d^2, d^7 and d^3, d^8 tetrahedral complexes is exactly the same as for d^1, d^6, etc., and can be taken for granted at this stage.

Whether or not the model is as good for tetrahedral complexes as for octahedral is not clearcut since, e.g., it is not possible to get d^1 tetrahedral complexes of a simple type and the $d^9(Cu^{2+})$ have other complications.

(vi) Potential Fields of Lower Symmetry

It is possible to calculate energy-level patterns for any nuclear configuration, e.g., square planar (27, 28) or linear. However, in general, such a calculation requires at least one parameter in addition to Dq (not to mention X, the $^3F - ^3P$ interval), so that the predictive power is small except in the sense that it (the model) can be applied to a wide range of different complexes to test its general self-consistency. This short discussion of Crystal Field Theory (CFT) is not meant to go so far as the solution of these problems; once the general ideas have been been assimilated the more advanced texts can be consulted for guidance in this matter (8, 12, 13).

C. LIGAND FIELD THEORY

It has become customary to use the term "Ligand Field Theory," which will be abbreviated to LFT, when referring to phenomena in which the ligands exert some specific effect that cannot be fully represented by a simple point charge or directed dipolar potential. Such things as covalent bonding, whether of σ or π type, are included under such a heading, since the CFT merely ignores the essentially σ bonded metal-ligand bond and replaces it by a simple potential. It is clear from much experimental evidence that it is not always possible to disregard such bonding, particularly when considering transitions that might concern either σ or π type electrons on the ligands.

The approach is, therefore, mainly a molecular orbital one, simplified in the direction of CFT because of the difficulty of getting simple numbers out as answers. The main problem, and the main answers, concern the type of molecular orbitals it is possible to set up for a complexed central ion. This matter will be considered now.

(i) Metal Orbitals

The problem is to find out which of the metal orbitals can participate in binding with the ligand orbitals and also, what type of bonds can be formed by them, i.e., σ or π or δ, etc. (The general methods of doing this are well outlined in references *3* and *29*, but will be briefly presented here for clarity.) The irreducible representations of the octahedral point group O (the inclusion of the center of symmetry thus using O_h is unnecessary since all orbitals built of $s, d, g \dots$ electrons will be gerade and all those built of $p, f, h \dots$ electrons will be ungerade). together with the symmetry operations are given in Table 1.2. There are two sets

TABLE 1.2. CHARACTER TABLE FOR THE
POINT GROUP O

	E	$8C_3$	$3C_2$	$6C_2'$	$6C_4$
A_1	1	1	1	1	1
A_2	1	1	1	-1	-1
E	2	-1	2	0	0
$T_1(x, y, z)$	3	0	-1	-1	$+1$
T_2	3	0	-1	$+1$	-1

of twofold axes, those along the x, y, z axes (the ligand-metal bond directions), and those at 45° to these axes and in the plane of two of them. The former of these is labelled C_2 and the latter C_2'.

TABLE 1.3.

	E	$4C_3^{\pm}$	$3C_2$	$6C_2'$	$3C_4^{\pm}$
s	1	1	1	1	1
p	3	0	-1	-1	1
d	5	-1	1	1	-1

The effect of operating on the s, p and d sets of orbitals is given in Table 1.3 in terms of the reducible representation χ. Comparison of χ for the s orbital with the irreducible representations for point group O in Table 1.2 shows that the s orbital is totally symmetrical, a_1, with respect to point group O and is, therefore, capable of forming σ bonds only.

Either by inspection or by the formal method of breaking up the reducible representation into irreducible representations it can be seen that

$$\chi = 0 \times a_1 + 0 \times e + 1 \times t_1 + 0 \times t_2$$

with respect to the point group O, and must be t_{1u} in O_h

[Formally,

$$n(i) = \frac{1}{h} \sum_R \chi(R)\chi_i(R)$$

i.e.,

$$n(t_1) = \frac{1}{24} [9 + 0 + 3 + 6 + 6]$$

$$= 1$$

and

$$n(a_1) = n(a_2) = n(e) = n(t_2) = 0]$$

Similarly, for d electrons

$$\chi = \chi(e) + \chi(t_2)$$

and in O_h, since d electrons are gerade, then these will be e_g and t_{2g} since, clearly, these are the two subshells into which the d shell splits when subjected to an octahedral perturbation.

Thus, the s, p, d sets of orbitals belong to the a_{1g}, t_{1u}, e_g, and t_{2g} irreducible representations of the point group O_h.

(ii) Ligand σ Orbitals

Consider now the possible MO's which the ligand σ orbitals could form. Representing them as blobs having axial symmetry as in Fig. 1.12 it can be seen that

$\chi(\sigma) =$	6	0	2	0	2

and this reducible representation breaks up to give

$$\chi(\sigma) = \chi(a_1) + \chi(e) + \chi(t_1)$$

and if the full group O_h is used it will be seen that the symmetries are a_{1g}, e_g, and t_{1u}. Thus it is possible to construct σ orbitals from $s(a_{1g})$, $p(t_{1u})$ and $d(e_g)$ orbitals of the central metal and these can overlap with the a_{1g}, t_{1u}, and e_g combinations of ligand orbitals. Alternatively, it is possible to consider the central metal orbitals "hybridizing" to form $d_\gamma{}^2 sp^3$ hybrids, where d_γ stands for $d(e_g)$, and these then form σ bonds individually with the σ orbitals of the ligands.

It is easy once again to find the actual form of the *ligand* linear combinations, from the symmetry operations. In Table 1.4 are shown the linear combinations

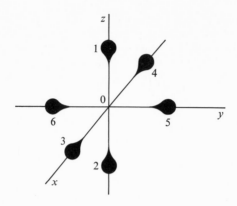

FIGURE 1.12.

TABLE 1.4.

Represen-tation in O_h	Ligand MO's		Central ion Orbitals
	σ	π	
a_{1g}	$\frac{1}{\sqrt{6}}(\phi_1 + \phi_2 + \phi_3 + \phi_4 + \phi_5 + \phi_6)$		n_s
e_g	$\frac{1}{3\sqrt{2}}(2\phi_1 + 2\phi_2 - \phi_3 - \phi_4 - \phi_5 - \phi_6)$		nd_{z^2}
	$\frac{1}{2}(\phi_3 + \phi_4 + \phi_5 - \phi_6)$		$nd_{x^2-y^2}$
t_{2g}		$\frac{1}{2}(\pi_{x1} - \pi_{x2} + \pi_{z3} - \pi_{z4})$	nd_{xz}
		$\frac{1}{2}(\pi_{y1} - \pi_{y2} + \pi_{z5} - \pi_{z6})$	nd_{yz}
		$\frac{1}{2}(\pi_{x5} - \pi_{x6} + \pi_{y3} - \pi_{y4})$	nd_{xy}
t_{1u}	$\frac{1}{\sqrt{2}}(\phi_3 - \phi_4)$	$\frac{1}{2}(\pi_{x1} + \pi_{x2} + \pi_{x5} + \pi_{x6})$	np_x
	$\frac{1}{\sqrt{2}}(\phi_5 - \phi_6)$	$\frac{1}{2}(\pi_{y1} + \pi_{y2} + \pi_{y3} + \pi_{y4})$	np_y
	$\frac{1}{\sqrt{2}}(\phi_1 - \phi_2)$	$\frac{1}{2}(\pi_{z3} + \pi_{z4} + \pi_{z5} + \pi_{z6})$	np_z
t_{2u}		$\frac{1}{2}(\pi_{x5} + \pi_{x6} - \pi_{x1} - \pi_{x2})$	
		$\frac{1}{2}(\pi_{y3} + \pi_{y4} - \pi_{y1} - \pi_{y2})$	
		$\frac{1}{2}(\pi_{z3} + \pi_{z4} - \pi_{z5} - \pi_{z6})$	
t_{1g}		$\frac{1}{2}(\pi_{z5} - \pi_{z6} - \pi_{y1} - \pi_{y2})$	
		$\frac{1}{2}(\pi_{z3} - \pi_{z4} - \pi_{x1} + \pi_{x2})$	
		$\frac{1}{2}(\pi_{y3} - \pi_{y4} - \pi_{x5} + \pi_{x6})$	

of ligand orbitals required to form ligand molecular orbitals appropriate to the octahedral point group O_h. In this table the numbering of the ligands is as given in Fig. 1.1. The σ orbitals on ligand i are designated by ϕ_i, while the $p\pi$ orbitals are designated π_{xi}, π_{yi}, etc. For the method of obtaining these, a more detailed text should be consulted (29).

(iii) Ligand π Orbitals

The possible π orbitals of the ligands can be found in precisely the same way as the σ orbitals

	E	C_3	C_2	C'_2	C_4
$\chi(\pi)$	12	0	-4	0	0

and this reduces to

$$\chi(\pi) = 2\chi(t_1) + 2\chi(t_2)$$

It is easy to show that both the t_1 and t_2 types must have both g and u representations, so that the complete set is t_{1g}, t_{1u}, t_{2g}, t_{2u} and simply from the number of nodes required to reproduce these symmetries the probable energy order is

$$t_{2g} < t_{1u} \sim t_{2u} < t_{1g}$$

The reasons why these MO forms have been calculated become clear if the form of the antibonding e_g sets are considered (30, 31) since these are the orbitals which are involved in most of the optical transitions and in the discussion of the magnetic properties of the complexes.

$$\sigma^*(e_g)\begin{cases} \psi_{x^2-y^2} = \alpha\, d_{x^2-y^2} - \beta \cdot \tfrac{1}{2}(\phi_3 + \phi_4 - \phi_5 - \phi_6) \\ \psi_{z^2} = \alpha\, d_{z^2} - \beta \cdot \dfrac{1}{3\sqrt{2}}(2\phi_1 + 2\phi_2 - \phi_3 - \phi_4 - \phi_5 - \phi_6) \end{cases}$$

and since $\alpha^2 + \beta^2 = 1$, $\beta = \sqrt{1 - \alpha^2}$, i.e.,

$$\begin{cases} \psi_{x^2-y^2} = \alpha\, d_{x^2-y^2} - \sqrt{1-\alpha^2}\,\tfrac{1}{2}(\phi_3 + \phi_4 - \phi_5 - \phi_6) \\ \psi_{z^2} = \alpha\, d_{z^2} - \dfrac{\sqrt{1-\alpha^2}}{2\sqrt{3}}(2\phi_1 + 2\phi_2 - \phi_3 - \phi_4 - \phi - \phi_6) \end{cases},$$

There are three "ideal" possibilities

(a) $\alpha = 1$

(b) $\alpha = \pm\tfrac{1}{2}$

(c) $\alpha = 0$

In the first, the d electron is completely on the central ion, i.e., there is no delocalization and the model is a crystal field one. In the second case the electron is equally shared between the metal and ligands and this corresponds to a "perfect" covalent bond without even any polarization, and finally, $\alpha = 0$ corresponds to the electron being completely on the ligands.

Experiment seems to show (31, 32) that the truth lies closer to $\alpha = 1$ in most cases, but without the use of MO's it is not possible to have even a small probability of the electron being found off the central metal ion.

The evidence requiring some delocalization of charge will be discussed in (v) below.

(iv) Ligand Field Orbital Diagrams

It is now possible to draw up the LF equivalents of the simple CF energy diagrams, with the simplification that it is too complex to represent the changes in the splittings with increasing "Dq" or covalent binding or, quite generally, perturbation of the central ion, so a simpler approach will be used.

In Fig. 1.13 is drawn a schematic set of molecular energy levels for an octahedral complex which are correlated with the isolated ion and isolated ligand energy levels (33, 34). All that can be hoped of such a diagram at the present stage of understanding is that the *order* of the levels should be correct, at least with regard to those levels for which some experimental evidence is available, whether it be from spectra, epr., or magnetic measurements.

The σ, π, and non-bonded levels shown for the isolated ligand are degenerate in the situation where the ligand is a monatomic ion (e.g. Cl^-, O^{2-}, etc.) and the degeneracy actually shown for the π orbitals is only true provided the ligand is cylindrically symmetrical (e.g., CO, NO, etc. *if* the $M-X-O$ bond is linear).

Fig. 1.14 gives a similar diagram (35, 36) for a tetrahedral complex such as $[MnO_4]^-$, $[CoCl_4]^{2-}$ etc., and the same restrictions apply here as for the octahedron, viz., that the molecule is strictly of the point group T_d with either monatomic ions or colinear $M-X-O$ bonds.

The tetrahedral diagram is somewhat in doubt, even with regard to the order of the energy levels, but in one respect it is somewhat simpler than the corresponding octahedral diagram. Whereas it is possible to compound an orbital of symmetry t_1 from the four ligands (see Table 1.5 for the symmetries pertinant to the tetrahedral point group T_d), it is not possible to obtain any orbital of such a symmetry from either s, p, or d central metal orbitals (one *can* be obtained from f orbitals) in a tetrahedral perturbing field. The atomic or ligand orbitals which are used to form such an orbital are essentially non-bonding with respect to the metal–ligand bond so that, in the first place, they are not shared in any way by the metal orbital and in the second place, their removal is unlikely to cause large changes in metal–ligand bond force constants. This places one of the MO's near the non-bonding region of energy and must increase the likelihood of such electrons being involved in the longest wavelength spectral transitions. If this is the case, then the properties of the orbital into which the excited electron goes should be readily shown by the nature of the transition observed and the symmetry of such a level might well turn out to be unambiguously determinable.

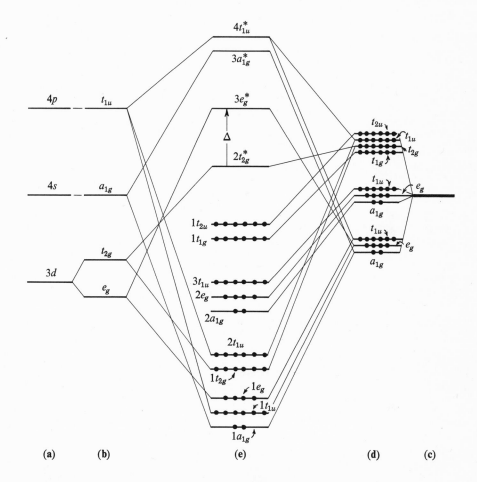

FIGURE 1.13.
    (a) field-free ion orbitals
    (b) symmetry orbitals (incipient molecule formation)
    (c) field-free monatomic ion orbitals
    (d) symmetry orbitals (incipient molecule formation)
    (e) molecular orbitals of complex

It must be remembered, also, that since the tetrahedron does not have a center of symmetry, the Laporte rule does not prohibit any transition, and so it frequently happens that the tetrahedral analogue of some particular transition in an octahedral molecule is fully allowed. (See for example the $^4T_{1g} \leftarrow {}^4A_{2g}$

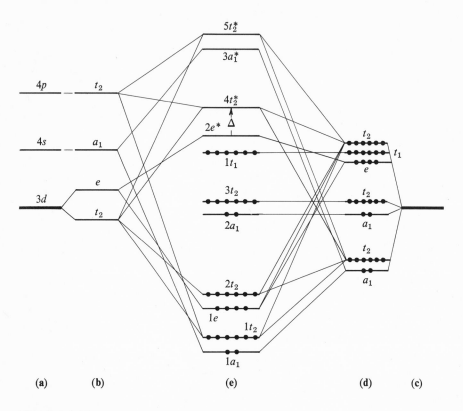

FIGURE 1.14.
  (a) field-free ion orbitals
  (b) symmetry orbitals (incipient molecule formation)
  (c) field-free monatomic ion orbitals
  (d) symmetry orbitals (incipient molecule formation)
  (e) molecular orbitals of complex

transition in Cr^{3+} complexes whose analogue in the tetrahedral case is the $^4T_1 \leftarrow {}^4A_2$ transition of Co^{2+} complexes and this is fully electric dipole allowed.)

Thus, the intensities of the tetrahedral complexes are generally about a factor of 100^x as great as those of the octahedral analogues and this is one distinguishing mark of the tetrahedral complexes. Because the intensities are so much higher, the tetrahedral complexes behave less like field-free atoms or ions than do the octahedral and the spectra of the former are not as well understood as those of the latter. It is possible to look at this aspect of octahedral versus tetrahedral in another way: in octahedral crystal fields, since a center of symmetry is preserved, it is not possible for atomic orbitals which are adjacent to one another energetically to interact or mix with each other. Table 1.5 shows the species into which each of the atomic orbitals splits in both octahedral and tetrahedral fields, and

TABLE 1.5. CORRELATION TABLE SHOWING THE IRREDUCIBLE REPRESENTATIONS IN POINT GROUPS O_h and T_d INTO WHICH THE ONE-ELECTRON ATOMIC ORBITALS SPLIT IN OCTAHEDRAL AND TETRAHEDRAL FIELDS, RESPECTIVELY

Point Group A.O.	O_h	T_d
s	a_{1g}	a_1
p	t_{1u}	t_2
d	$e_g + t_{2g}$	$e + t_2$
f	$a_{2u} + t_{1u} + t_{2u}$	$a_2 + t_2 + t_1$
g	$a_{1g} + e_g + t_{1g} + t_{2g}$	$a_1 + e + t_1 + t_2$

it will be noticed that whereas a p orbital transforms like t_{1u} and a d orbital splits to give t_{2g} and e_g under O_h symmetry, yet both yield a t_2 irreducible representation in T_d symmetry. This means that perturbing atomic energy levels by a noncentrosymmetric field of the tetrahedral type will cause a very rapid departure of any properties of the perturbed atom which depend upon their original pure atomic forms. On the other hand, it will be observed that the only similar situation is the octahedral field is that both p and f orbitals yield a t_{1u} representation and these levels (p and f) are energetically an order of magnitude further apart than the p and d so that the properties of the octahedrally perturbed ion might be expected to depart much more slowly from those of the isolated free ion.

(v) Use of Ligand Field Theory rather than Crystal Field Theory

The reasons why it is necessary to use LFT rather than the much more simple CFT will not be given in detail here. They will become clearer when the optical and esr spectra and the magnetism of complex ions are discussed in detail later, but, essentially, there are five main reasons.

1. In the interpretation of the optical spectra of inorganic complexes it appears that the magnitude of the term interval $'F - 'P$ has decreased considerably in the complex compared with the free ion, i.e., the Slater–Condon F_i or Racah parameters A, B, C are lower than their free-ion values (*31, 32, 37, 38*).

2. The esr spectra (*38, 39*) suggest that the spin-orbit coupling constant of the "central ion" in a complex is much lower than in the free ion.
3. The orbital contribution to the magnetic moment appears to be reduced when compared with the free ion (*40, 41*).
4. In the complex $[IrCl_6]^{2-}$, which has the configuration t_{2g}^5 viewed as a simple complexed ion, hyperfine interaction is observed in the esr spectrum (*42*), indicating a coupling of the "odd" t_{2g} electron with the nuclear spin of the chlorine nucleus.
5. In the nmr spectrum (*43*) of MnF_2 the F^{19} resonance frequency is shifted appreciably from its F^- ion value, owing to "spin polarization" effects.

(vi) Strong-Field Theory   (*25, 8, 10, 12, 13*)

By starting the perturbation calculations with the free-ion term wavefunctions, as was done in the previous sections, it is implicitly assumed that the electron repulsion energies are, on the whole, larger than the crystal field perturbation energies (since it is the electron repulsion energies which separate the various terms of the field-free ion from one another). Certain experimental evidence, mainly the magnetism of complexes of the $[Fe(CN)_6]^{3-}$ type, can be understood only if it is assumed that the crystal field strength is larger than the electron repulsion energies.

It is not possible to be too dogmatic about what magnitude of crystal field strength will achieve such an effect but, in general, if $Dq \gtrsim 2800$–3000 cm^{-1} for a central ion which is formally tripositive, then such a state of affairs will apply. Alternatively, if $Dq \lesssim 1500$–1750 cm^{-1} for the same oxidation state of central ion, then the weak-field approximation will give reasonable results. Intermediate cases are best considered on their merits.

In the strong-field approximation the d orbital set is considered to be subjected to a strong octahedral field, splitting the fivefold degenerate level into the t_{2g} and e_g levels, as was found for the d^1 case (where, of course, there are no interelectronic repulsion effects to be considered), and the electrons in the polyelectron cases are then considered to be assigned to these new "orbitals" in exactly the same way as with a field-free atom or ion. In other words, the t_{2g} level, being lower, is first filled with three electrons having parallel spins and then, before the e_g level is filled, three more electrons with opposite spins are added. Only then is the e_g level filled.

This is tantamount to assuming that the distance apart, energetically, of the t_{2g} and e_g levels (often called the d_ε and d_γ levels in the strong-field case) is larger than the interelectronic repulsion energies. This distance has, roughly, the value given above (i.e., $10\ Dq \equiv \Delta \sim 28{,}000$–30,000 cm^{-1} for a tripositive ion). The most spectacular effect of this is that the maximum of the spin quantum number S is 3/2 instead of 5/2 for a field-free or weak-field ion, and Fe^{3+} in a complex such as ferricyanide has only one unpaired electron spin, compared with five in the free ion or in the weak-field case (*44, 45*). Thus it should be that the spectra and magnetism support one another in such an interpretation and, in the main, this turns out to be so.

Under such conditions it is more convenient to use an orbital set which has well-defined quantum numbers in a cubic field, and so instead of specifying the m_l values of the orbitals, linear combinations of these one electron functions are used—in particular, those already defined and derived in section B (ii) (page 16) and represented in Fig. 1.3. [These orbitals are often written d_{ε_1}, d_{ε_2}, d_{ε_3}, and d_{γ_1}, d_{γ_2}, or ξ, η, ζ and u, v and it will be noted by comparing the real forms of the d wavefunctions in section A (i) (page 4) with those as defined on page 16, that they are identical. It is this identity which allowed the physical picture of certain orbitals being more affected by the ligand electrons—or simple negative charges—than others, to be used in an "intuitive" way.]

The way in which the final levels are obtained from the $d_\varepsilon d_\gamma$ configurations is fully dealt with elsewhere (8, 12, 13) and will not be repeated here. Of course, it does not matter which approach is used for intermediate cases, since the same answer will result; the strong-field limit has, however, the pictorial advantage, which is often helpful, but may lead to erroneous conclusions if its use is not verified by a more formal approach.

Probably the best example of this is the oft-repeated assertion that "a negative ion attacking an octahedral complex will approach the complex along a line from the metal ion to the center of the octahedron face (cube vertex!) because it is there that the d electron density is lowest." Such a statement can be disproved easily if the magnitude of $\Theta(\theta)\Phi(\varphi)$ is calculated for the d_ε shell and compared with the maximum value found for any direction in a field-free ion.

Using the set of functions normalized to 4π, viz.,

$$\left.\begin{array}{l} d_{z^2} \equiv \sqrt{\dfrac{5}{2}}\,(3\cos^2\theta - 1) \\[4mm] d_{x^2-y^2} \equiv \sqrt{\dfrac{15}{2}}\,\sin^2\theta\cos 2\varphi \end{array}\right\} d_\gamma$$

$$\left.\begin{array}{l} d_{xy} \equiv \sqrt{\dfrac{15}{2}}\,\sin^2\theta\sin 2\varphi \\[3mm] d_{xz} \equiv \sqrt{15}\,\sin\theta\cos\theta\cos\varphi \\[3mm] d_{yz} \equiv \sqrt{15}\,\sin\theta\cos\theta\sin\varphi \end{array}\right\} d_\varepsilon$$

The magnitude of $\Theta(\theta)\Phi(\varphi)$ along the 111 axis

$$= \sqrt{\frac{15}{3}}\left\{\frac{\sin^2\theta\sin 2\varphi}{2} + \sin\theta\cos\theta\cos\varphi + \sin\theta\cos\theta\sin\varphi\right\}$$

and $\quad \theta = 54° 44'$, i.e., $\dfrac{109° 28'}{2}$

$\varphi = 45°$

$= \sqrt{5}\,(0.\dot{3} + 0.\dot{6})$

$= \sqrt{5}$

This result could have been anticipated without calculation, since there is no contribution along this axis from either d_{z^2} or $d_{x^2-y^2}$—in the former, since $\cos^2 54° 44' = 0.\dot{3}$ and in the latter, since $\cos 2\varphi = 0$; thus, in a field-free atom, the complete contribution, which is $\sqrt{5}$ using the set of functions given above, comes only from the d_ε orbitals so that the magnitude is the same for the d_ε orbitals as in the free atom or ion. The value $\sqrt{5}$ is the maximum possible so that the angular probability of finding an electron is just as great along the 111 axis as for a line through the center of the cube edge.

REFERENCES

1. S. Glasstone, *Theoretical Chemistry*, Van Nostrand, Princeton, N.J., 1944.
2. H. E. White, *Introduction to Atomic Spectra*, McGraw-Hill, New York, 1934.
3. H. Eyring, J. Walter and G. E. Kimball, *Quantum Chemistry*, Wiley, New York, 1944.
4. W. Moore, *Physical Chemistry*, 3d ed., Prentice-Hall, Englewood Cliffs, N.J., 1962.
5. G. Herzberg, *Atomic Spectra and Atomic Structure*, Prentice-Hall, Englewood Cliffs, N.J., 1934.
6. C. E. Moore, "Atomic Energy Levels," *Nat. Bu. Stand.* [467], **1**.
7. F. E. Ilse and H. Hartmann, *Z. Physik. Chem.* **197**: 239 (1951).
8. C. J. Ballhausen, *Introduction to Ligand Field Theory*, McGraw-Hill, New York, 1962.
9. H. Bethe, *Ann. Physik.* [5], **3**: 135 (1929).
10. T. M. Dunn, "The Visible and Ultra-violet Spectra of Complex Compounds," in J. Lewis and R. Wilkins (eds.), *Modern Coordination Chemistry*, Interscience, New York, 1960, chap. IV.
11. T. M. Dunn, "Appraisal of Experiment and Theory in the Spectra of Complexes," *Pure and Appl. Chem.* **6**: 1 (1963).
12. J. S. Griffith, *The Theory of Transition Metal Ions*, Cambridge University Press, Cambridge, 1961.
13. C. K. Jorgensen, *Absorption Spectra and Chemical Bonding in Complexes*, Pergamon Press, Oxford, 1962.
14. C. K. Jorgensen, *Orbitals in Atoms and Molecules*, Academic Press, New York, 1962.
15. D. S. McClure, *Solid State Phys.* **9**: 400 (1959).

16. L. E. Orgel, *An Introduction to Transition Metal Chemistry*, Methuen, London, 1960.
17. R. L. Carlin and T. S. Piper, *J. Chem. Phys.* **35**: 1809 (1961).
18. O. G. Holmes and D. S. McClure, *J. Chem. Phys.* **26**: 1686 (1957).
19. L. E. Orgel, *J. Chem. Phys.* **23**: 1004 (1955).
20. C. K. Jorgensen, in *Inst. Intern. de Chim. Solvay*, 10ᵉ *Conseil de Chim.* (Brussels) 1956, p. 355.
21. J. C. Slater, *The Quantum Theory of Atomic Structure*, McGraw-Hill, New York, 1961, vols. I and II.
22. R. Finkelstein and J. H. VanVleck, *J. Chem. Phys.* **8**: 790 (1940).
23. C. J. Ballhausen and A. D. Liehr, *Ann. Phys.* (N.Y.) **6**: 134 (1959).
24. D. L. Wood, J. Ferguson, K. Knox and J. F. Dillon Jr., *J. Chem. Phys.* **39**: 890 (1963).
25. Y. Tanabe and S. Sugano, *J. Phys. Soc.* (*Japan*) **9**: 753 (1954).
26. L. E. Orgel, *J. Chem. Phys.* **23**: 1004 (1955).
27. C. J. Ballhausen, *Kgl. Danske Videnskab. Selskab, Mat-Fys. Medd.* **29**: 4 (1954).
28. J. S. Griffith and L. E. Orgel, *J. Chem. Soc.* **1956**: 4981.
29. F. A. Cotton, *Chemical Applications of Group Theory*, Wiley, New York, 1963.
30. J. H. Van Vleck, *J. Chem. Phys.* **3**: 807 (1935).
31. J. Owen, *Proc. Roy. Soc.* **A227**: 183 (1955).
32. T. M. Dunn, *J. Chem. Soc.* **1959**: 623.
33. A. D. Liehr, *Progress Inorg. Chem.* **3**: 281 (1962).
34. A. D. Liehr, *J. Chem. Educ.* **39**: 135 (1962).
35. A. Carrington and C. K. Jorgensen, *Mol. Phys.* **4**: 395 (1961).
36. A. D. Liehr, *J. Chem. Educ.* **39**: 135 (1962).
37. C. K. Jorgensen, *Discussions Faraday Soc.* [26]: **110** (1958).
38. A. Abragam and M. H. L. Pryce, *Proc. Roy. Soc.* **A206**: 164, 173 (1951).
39. J. H. Griffiths and J. Owen, *Proc. Roy. Soc.*, **A213**: 459 (1952).
40. R. Schlapp and W. A. Penney, *Phys. Rev.* **42**: 666 (1932).
41. O. Jordahl, *Phys. Rev.* **45**: 87 (1934).
42. J. H. E. Griffiths, J. Owen, and I. M. Ward, *Proc. Roy. Soc.* **A219**: 526 (1953).
43. R. G. Shulman and V. Jaccarino, *Phys. Rev.* **109**: 1084 (1958).
44. J. H. Van Vleck, *J. Chem. Phys.* **3**: 807 (1935).
45. J. B. Howard, *J. Chem. Phys.* **3**: 813 (1935).

CHAPTER 2 THE OPTICAL SPECTRA
OF INORGANIC COMPLEXES

THOMAS M. DUNN

A. OCTAHEDRAL COMPLEXES

(i) Crystal Field Transitions

Crystal field transitions are defined to be transitions from levels that are exclusively perturbed d orbitals to levels of the same kind, i.e., the electron is originally entirely localized on the central ion and remains so in the excited state. These transitions may be one of two types, either those which originate *and* terminate upon levels arising from the *same* term of the free ion, or those which terminate upon a level "originating" from a different term of the field-free ion. In the former case, the transition energy tends to zero as Dq tends to zero; in the latter case, the transition energy approaches the interterm separation energy of the field-free ion.

The reason for distinguishing between these two types is that the magnitude of Dq can be obtained only from the former type or, at most, by the subtraction of two transition energies when the two transitions terminate upon levels of this type (see, e.g., Mn^{2+}).

The only selection rule that has any bearing upon which transitions are seen is the $\Delta S = 0$ rule. While it does not, in fact, entirely prohibit transitions when $\Delta S \neq 0$ (say, $\Delta S = \pm 1$) nonetheless, such transitions are, at most, only a tenth as strong as the spin-allowed ones. Perusal of the point group character tables (*1*) for O_h shows that for a transition to be allowed for electric dipole radiation,

the direct product of the ground and excited state symmetries must transform
(1) like T_{1u}. Since all the crystal field states are gerade (g), this clearly impossible,
and it has been known since 1937 (2) that, under such circumstances, the transition appears only if some nontotally symmetric vibration of the right symmetry
distorts either the ground or excited-states shapes to such an extent as to at
least remove the center of symmetry. The details of this vibrational-electronic
("vibronic") interaction will not be considered further here, since the matter
is one of complexity (3) and the details are not pertinent to the main lines of discussion.

It does seem, however, that such a vibration will always allow the crystal
field transitions to appear, albeit weakly. In the first transition series of octahedral complexes, the molar extinction coefficient of the transitions range from
as low as ~0.01 in manganese II complexes to as high as ~25–30 for some (non-
chelate) complexes of cobalt III and nickel II. The tetrahedral analogues are
more intense by anything from a factor of ~50 to ~200 because of the removal
of the center of symmetry.

It is not the purpose of this discussion to deal fully with every complex and
every electron configuration, but simply to outline the main assignments and to
comment where necessary. One example of each configuration will be dealt with
as a guide, where such a spectrum has been satisfactorily analyzed or assigned.

(a) d^1 and d^6 (i.e., t_{2g}^1 and $t_{2g}^4 e_g^2$)

From energy-level diagrams, calculated as in Chapter 1, it is clear that only
one intraconfigurational d transition is possible (with $\Delta S = 0$) and the transi-
tion† is $E_g \leftarrow T_{2g}^*$ (it being "doublet" for d^1 and "quintet" for d^6).

The spectrum of $[Ti(H_2O)_6]^{3+}$ is reproduced in Fig. 2.1(a). It will be observed
that it consists of a rather broad hump of absorption with a maximum at
20,300 cm^{-1} (~4900 Å) and a shoulder at ~17,500 cm^{-1}. The intensity is low,
$\varepsilon_{max} \sim 5$ and the oscillator strength, f, of the transition is ~10^{-4}. The double
nature of the band, i.e., the shoulder, is at present considered to be caused by a
nuclear configurational instability in the excited state, i.e., by the Jahn–Teller
effect (3, 4). As remarked previously, this transition has an energy of $10Dq$ so
that $Dq \sim 2000$ cm^{-1} for $[Ti(H_2O)_6]^{3-}$.

The spectrum (5) of $[CoF_6]^{3-}$ has been reproduced in Fig. 2.1(b). It will be
observed that it is also "double" in appearance, with an absolute energy close
to 13,000 cm^{-1}. From other evidence it is known that Co III tends to have
somewhat higher Dq values for its complexes than the analogous Titanium III
complexes, so that the low Dq value of ~1300 cm^{-1} must be a reflection of the
weak perturbation which fluoride ion has as a ligand.

---

† The accepted spectroscopic practice of placing the excited state first, when discussing
transitions, will be followed in this chapter.

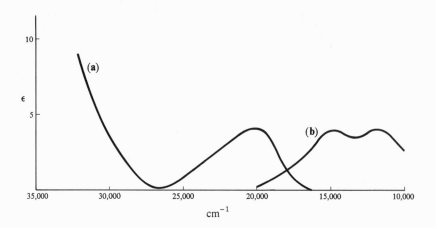

FIGURE 2.1.
  (a) spectrum of Cs Ti(SO₄)₂ 12H₂O, i.e., [Ti(H₂O)₆]³⁺
  (b) spectrum of K₃Co F₆ solid, i.e., [Co F₆]³⁻

(b) d^4 and d^9 (i.e., $t_{2g}{}^3 e_g{}^1$ and $t_{2g}{}^6 e_g{}^3$)

Only one transition occurs in these cases also, being $^{5,2}T_{2g} \leftarrow {}^{5,2}E_g$ in type, the quintet referring to d^4 and the doublet to d^9. Cr II, Mn III, and Fe IV all have a d^4 configuration, but octahedral complexes having these central ions are not common. The spectrum of the species presumed (6) to be [Cr(H₂O)₆]²⁺ is given in Fig. 2.2(a); it will be observed that it is rather similar in appearance to the d^1, d^6 transitions. The transition found at $\sim 14{,}000$ cm⁻¹ is the only one that could be attributed to a crystal field band with the assignment $^5T_{2g} \leftarrow {}^5E_g$. The same is true for the transition at 10,000–14,000 cm⁻¹ in the d^9 complex (7) [Cu(H₂O)₄]SO₄H₂O (Fig. 2.2(b)). The transitions are very broad, particularly in the latter case, and it is probable that the bands observed arise from at least two species, [Cu(H₂O)₆]²⁺ and [Cu(H₂O)₄]²⁺ coordinated by a sulphate group in the fifth position (perhaps also the complex [Cu(H₂O)₄]²⁺, but this is unknown).

Not much can be said about these d^1, d^6, d^4, d^9 spectra since there are no other spin-allowed bands which can be predicted and checked experimentally. The only things in favor of their assignment as given are (a) over a range of energy from the infrared to the near ultraviolet, only one band appears in anything like a reasonable place energetically and is permissive evidence in favor of the assignment, and (b) all the bands have much the same appearance, indicating some common factor in their origin.

In the d^4 and d^6 configurations it is formally possible for transitions to occur with $\Delta S = -1$ (i.e., $\Delta r = -2$) and, in addition, some complexes are also known where the strong-field limit must be used [e.g., $K_4Cr(CN)_6 \cdot 3H_2O$ which has

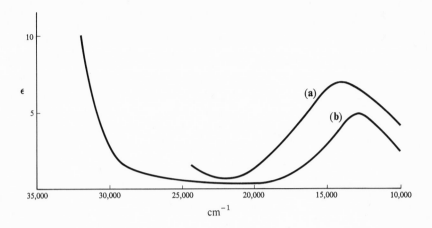

FIGURE 2.2.
(a) spectrum of $(Cr(H_2O)_6]^{2+}$ ion
(b) spectrum of $CuSO_4 \, 5H_2O$ solid

two unpaired spins (8)—i.e., a spin triplet is lowest lying, and in cobalt III complexes, most are diamagnetic (8) indicating that a ^1A state is lowest]. The transitions in such cases are sometimes difficult to assign because of overlying charge transfer bands (see below), but many assignments have been made on the basis of the complete energy-level diagrams calculated by Tanabe and Sugano (see Figs. 2.3, 2.4, 2.5, 2.6, 2.7, 2.8, 2.9). These diagrams are exactly the same as the earlier ones (Chapter 1, pp. 18, 21), except that the ground state is always represented horizontally and their calculation includes many of the lower-multiplicity terms of the ion so that they are somewhat more complete than the simpler diagrams.† In using them it must be remembered that they are constructed with the aid of many simplifying assumptions and so should not be taken quantitatively. Rather, they should be used as a guide to what CF transitions might be expected to appear in any particular region of the spectrum.

(c) d^2 and d^7 (i.e., t_{2g}^2 and $t_{2g}^5 e_g^2$ roughly)

The spectrum of $[V(H_2O)_6]^{3+}$ is a good example (9) of the d^2 configuration (see Fig. 2.12). There are weak broad bands ($\varepsilon \sim 6$) at 17,700 cm^{-1}(5800 Å) and 25,000 cm^{-1}(4000 Å) and the former of these is assigned as $^3T_{2g}(F) \leftarrow {}^3T_{1g}(F)$, from the diagrams Fig. 1.9 or Fig. 2.3. The assignment of the latter band is almost certainly $^3T_{1g}(P) \leftarrow {}^3T_{1g}(F)$ and even a rough value of Dq estimated from the lowest frequency transition puts the transition $^3A_{2g} \leftarrow {}^3T_{1g}(F)$ at about

---

† Also, the use of the symbol F in the diagrams for a triply degenerate electronic state instead of T as in the rest of the text is in conformity with general spectroscopic notation even though T has been more commonly employed to avoid confusion with atomic F terms.

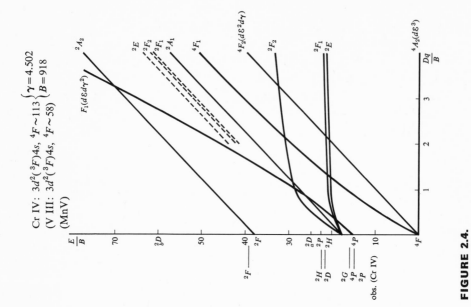

FIGURE 2.4.
energy diagram for d^3

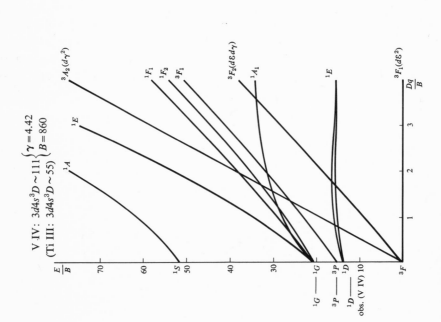

FIGURE 2.3.
energy diagram for d^2

42

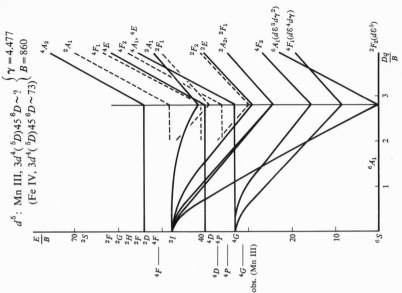

FIGURE 2.6.
energy diagram for d^5

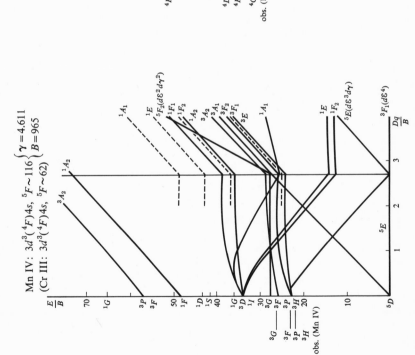

FIGURE 2.5.
energy diagram for d^4

43

d^7: Co III: $3d^6(^5D)4s$, $^6D \sim 48$ $\left\{ \begin{array}{l} \gamma = 4.633 \\ B = 971 \end{array} \right.$
(Ni IV: $3d^6(^5D)4s$, $^6D \sim$?)

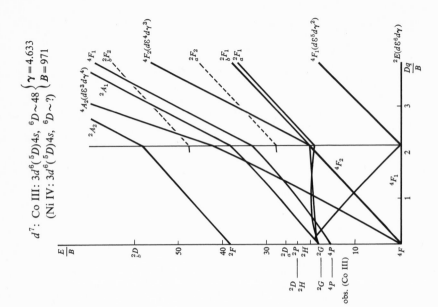

FIGURE 2.8.
energy diagram for d^7

Co IV: $3d^5(^6S)4s$, $^7S \sim$? $\left\{ \begin{array}{l} \gamma = 4.808 \\ B = 1,065 \end{array} \right.$
(Fe III: $3d^5(^6S)4s$, $^7S \sim 33$)

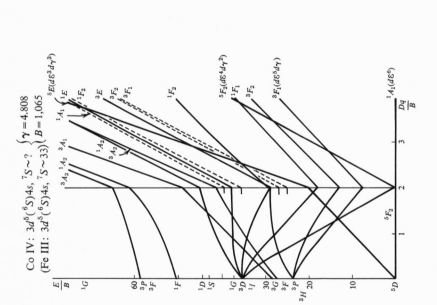

FIGURE 2.7.
energy diagram for d^6

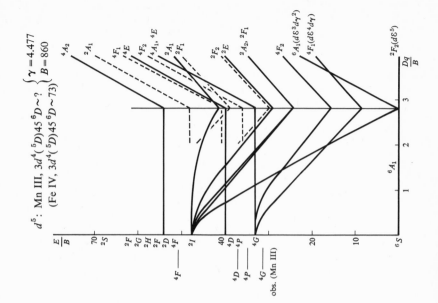

FIGURE 2.6.
energy diagram for d^5

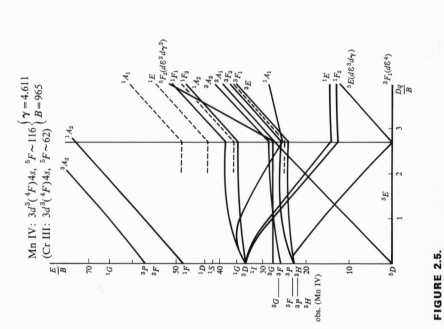

FIGURE 2.5.
energy diagram for d^4

43

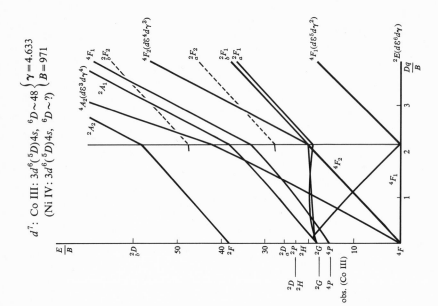

FIGURE 2.8.
energy diagram for d^7

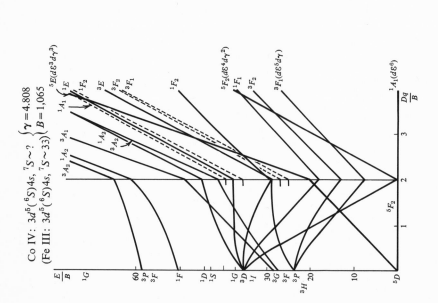

FIGURE 2.7.
energy diagram for d^6

44

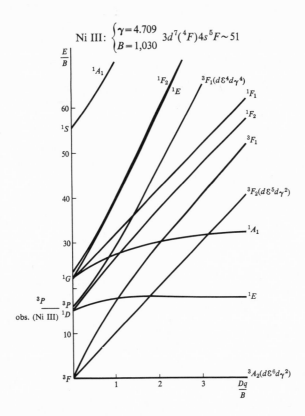

FIGURE 2.9.
energy diagram for d^8

37,000 cm^{-1} (2700 Å) where the region is somewhat obscured by charge transfer transitions.

The last transition is also expected to be very weak, since it corresponds, configurationally, to the simultaneous excitation of *two* electrons, i.e., $t_{2g}^2 \to e_g^2$ and may not appear at all, although its analogue has been assigned (correctly?) in cobalt II complexes. There is also a weak transition at about 34,500 cm^{-1}, but the assignment is in doubt. [Co(H$_2$O)$_6$]$^{2+}$ and Co(H$_2$O)$_4$Cl$_2$ spectra have been thoroughly examined and the transitions assigned (*10, 11*) as follows:

$$^4T_{2g}(F) \leftarrow {}^4T_{1g}(F) \qquad 8\text{–}9000 \text{ cm}^{-1}$$

$$^2E_g \qquad \leftarrow \qquad \sim 11,000 \text{ cm}^{-1}$$

$$^4A_{2g} \qquad \leftarrow \qquad 16\text{–}18,000 \text{ cm}^{-1}$$

$$^4T_{1g}(P) \leftarrow \qquad 20\text{–}21,000 \text{ cm}^{-1}$$

the transitions being much further to lower frequencies than the vanadium spectra, because of the lower oxidation state and the correspondingly smaller Dq values. ($Dq \sim 900$ cm^{-1}.)

The cobalt spectra have transitions assigned as spin-forbidden transitions and these, as expected, are much weaker than the spin-allowed bands.

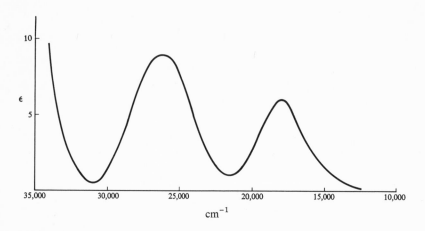

FIGURE 2.10.
spectrum of [V(H$_2$O)$_6$]$^{3+}$

(d) d^3 and d^8 (i.e., t_{2g}^3 and $t_{2g}^6 e_g^2$)

The complexes having these electron configurations have been more thoroughly examined than any other group. The main point about them is that they both have an A_{2g} ground term and this has no orbital angular momentum. Such complexes have no orbital degeneracy reasons for nuclear configurational distortion in their ground states (i.e., no Jahn–Teller distortion), and so are particularly interesting both optically and magnetically. The spectra have been assigned as follows (10, 12, 13), the spectrum of the ruby (Cr^{3+} in Al$_2$O$_3$) being one of the best known.

^2E_g	$\leftarrow ^4A_{2g}$	$\sim 15,000$ cm^{-1} in ruby
$^2T_{1g}$	$\leftarrow$	$\sim 15,500$ cm^{-1} in ruby
$^4T_{2g}$	$\leftarrow$	$\sim 17,500$ cm^{-1} in the hexahydrate
$^2T_{2g}$	$\leftarrow$	$22,000$ cm^{-1} in ruby
$^4T_{1g}(F)$	$\leftarrow$	$24,700$ cm^{-1} in the hexahydrate
$^4T_{1g}(P)?$	$\leftarrow$	$37,000$ cm^{-1} in the hexahydrate

For the hexahydrate, a value of $Dq \sim 1750$ cm^{-1} seems to fit the data best.

Nickel II is the main ion having a d^8 configuration and the hexaquo and hexamine complexes have been extensively studied (*14, 15, 16*). There are transitions at (amine values in parentheses, and hexaquo otherwise),

$$^3T_{2g} \leftarrow {}^3A_{2g} \qquad 8600 \text{ cm}^{-1} \ (10,700)$$

$$^3T_{1g}(F) \leftarrow \qquad\qquad 13,500 \text{ cm}^{-1} \ (17,500)$$

$$^3T_{1g}(P) \leftarrow \qquad\qquad 25,300 \text{ cm}^{-1} \ (28,200)$$

with transitions also at 15,400 cm^{-1} and 18,500 cm^{-1} which are almost certainly to be assigned as $^1E_g \leftarrow {}^3A_{2g}$ and $^1A_{1g} \leftarrow {}^3A_{2g}$, respectively.

The assignments for the first three transitions in the Cr^{3+} complex and the first transition, at least, in the nickel compound have been confirmed (*17*) from other than a theoretical *cum* empirical approach and so must be considered as certain. These assignments, together with the following ones for manganese II hexaquo complex, are sufficient to place the CF method in a very strong position with regard to proof of its essential correctness.

(e) d^5 (i.e., $t_{2g}{}^3e_g{}^2$ ground configuration)

This spectrum has been one of the most fruitful sources of information on the effects of coordinating ligands on the central ion. The spectrum of $[Mn(H_2O)_6]^{2+}$ is given in Fig. 2.11 and, at once, one difference between it and the other spectra will be noticed. This difference is the very sharp band at 25,000 cm^{-1} (4000 Å). As discussed in Chapter 1, none of the four quartet terms of Mn^{2+} are split in first order and, as Table 1.5 shows, the ^4G term gives $^4A_{1g}$, $^4T_{1g}$, ^4E_g and $^4T_{2g}$ terms in an octahedral field, even though all four have the same energy in first

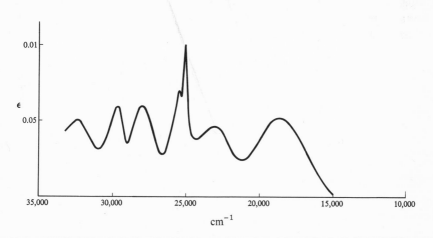

FIGURE 2.11.
spectrum of $[Mn(H_2O)_6]^{2+}$

order. Since there are no other $^4A_{1_g}$ terms which arise from ^4F, ^4D, or ^4P terms, this level should remain independent of Dq. In the Orgel diagram it can be seen that this is so, since it is simply parallel to the ground term $^6A_{1_g}$ energy level (which is, itself, unaffected).

In addition to the $^4A_{1_g}$ term, it happens fortuitously that the two ^4E_g terms— one from ^4G and the other from ^4D—are also independent of Dq, as is the $^4A_{2_g}$ term which arises from ^4F, since it is the only one of this species. The $^4A_{1_g}$ term and one of the ^4E_g terms are accidently degenerate in the octahedral CF approximation, so that there should be three different transitions which are independent of Dq.

The significance of a transition being independent of Dq is that it will be sharp (18), since, if there is a relative slope between two levels, there will be a range of Dq values which any assembly of molecules at a particular temperature will have at a particular time—bearing in mind that the ligands will be vibrating "against" the metal ion and that $D \propto a^{-5}$, i.e., Dq is very sensitive to the metal-ligand distance—and this will serve to broaden the band. Most CF transitions are, for this reason as well as others, rather broad and show little or no vibrational structure.

A narrow band in the spectrum should, therefore, be equated with a transition to one of the levels independent of Dq, and in the case of the transition at 25,000 cm^{-1}, to the ^4E_g, $^4A_{1_g}$ transition. There is a doubling seen in this sharp band and it is noteworthy in this respect that ^4E_g and $^4A_{1_g}$ are only degenerate if it is assumed that electrons in both the t_{2_g} and e_g shells have the same electron repulsion (Racah) parameters. Since this is certainly not so, a small split is to be expected. Caution is advisable, however, since it does not necessarily follow that the "doubling" which is observed is, in fact, due to this splitting—there being many other reasons why such a doubling can occur.

It might well be asked whether it is possible to get a physical picture as to why some of the transitions are independent of Dq. The answer is that such a picture *is* possible. The transitions which are Dq independent are essentially intraconfigurational—configurational in this sense being either t_{2_g} or e_g (not d as a whole). For example, the transitions shown in Fig. 1.10 (p. 23) in a configurational manner, are of such a type and the transition energy is, in effect, simply the difference in electron repulsion energy in the parallel-spin and spin-paired situations. For this reason, the frequency at which such a transition appears should be the same as in the free ion, but experiment shows that this is not true.

The transition at 25,000 cm^{-1} in $[Mn(H_2O)_6]^{2+}$ should occur at the same frequency as an atomic $^4G \leftarrow {}^6S$ transition of the free ion and this latter transition is known to be at 26,800 cm^{-1}. This shows that there has been a change in the magnitude of the interelectronic repulsion parameters B and C and reasons for this change must be sought. The magnitude of the reduction is only small in the ^4G term of Mn^{2+}, but such reductions are much larger—as large as 40 to 50 per cent of the free ion value in some cases—in many other complex ions and molecules. This will be discussed in more detail below, under Ligand Field effects.

There are two other transitions which are independent of Dq in Mn^{2+} complexes—the $^4E_g(D) \leftarrow {}^6A_{1g}$ and $^4A_{2g} \leftarrow {}^6A_{1g}$ transitions. These are also sharp, as the spectrum shows, although not as sharp as the 25,000 cm^{-1} transition, and it is likely that some second-order effects show up in these transitions a little more than in the 25,000 cm^{-1} case.

The complete assignment for the $[Mn(H_2O)_6]^{2+}$ spectrum is as follows (10, 19, 20):

$$^4T_{1g}(G) \leftarrow {}^6A_{1g} \qquad 18,800 \text{ cm}^{-1}$$
$$^4T_{2g}(G) \leftarrow \qquad 23,000 \text{ cm}^{-1}$$
$$^4E_g(G) \leftarrow \qquad 24,900 \text{ cm}^{-1}$$
$$^4A_{1g}(G) \leftarrow \qquad 25,150 \text{ cm}^{-1}$$
$$^4T_{2g}(D) \leftarrow \qquad 28,000 \text{ cm}^{-1}$$
$$^4E_g(D) \leftarrow \qquad 29,700 \text{ cm}^{-1}$$
$$^4T_{1g}(P) \leftarrow \qquad 32,400 \text{ cm}^{-1}$$
$$^4A_{2g}(F) \leftarrow \qquad 35,400 \text{ cm}^{-1}$$
$$^4T_{1g}(F) \leftarrow \qquad 36,900 \text{ cm}^{-1}$$
$$^4T_{2g}(F) \leftarrow \qquad 40,600 \text{ cm}^{-1}$$

It must be pointed out that it is not possible to predict the position of all these transitions using a single value of B and C and only one value of Dq. However, the deviations are relatively minor when it is recognized what gross simplifications have been made and also when it is realized that even for the free ion, the Racah theory does not give very good results in its simple form. (It is possible to get better results for the energy levels in the pure-ion case, but the methods are not, then, easily applicable to the CF model.)

It is not intended to discuss large numbers of spectra, but simply to indicate the overall scheme according to which the assignments are made. Many references (4, 13, 17, 21, 22, 23) exist which contain large numbers of spectra and which include a somewhat more complete discussion. These should be consulted for further details.

(f) Ligand field aspects of the spectra

It has been mentioned that there is a reduction in the magnitudes of the interelectronic repulsion energies of the central ion upon complex formation and that the magnitude of this reduction is often very large. Such a reduction is quite impossible using the electrostatic (CF) model outlined here and various suggestions have been made as to the reason(s) for this reduction. For the most part, what is required is an increase in the space in which the two representative electrons can move and this can be accomplished mainly in one of two ways. Either it can be imagined that the orbitals have expanded in size and remain strictly central metal d orbitals and/or it can be supposed that the central metal orbitals overlap with ligand orbitals of the appropriate symmetry and form molecular orbitals in which the space available for the electrons is larger, i.e., they spend only part of their time in the original metal orbitals and the rest is spent " delocalized or decentralized " in the ligand orbitals.

The most physical way of picturing the first process is by supposing that the central positive ion "polarizes" electrons off the ligands and so reduces its effective net positive charge. It is clear from the values of the Racah parameters, B and C, in the free ions themselves (24) that a charge reduction does decrease the interelectronic repulsion energies (for example, the ^4P-^4F separation has a value of $14,600 \text{ cm}^{-1}$ for Co II and only $11,200 \text{ cm}^{-1}$ for the isoelectronic Ni I; this interval equals $15B$, so that B is reduced from 973 cm^{-1} to 747 cm^{-1}, a decrease of 23 per cent) and the reductions are of the same order of magnitude in going from a free dipositive ion to a complex. In a slightly more sophisticated CF treatment, the part of the wavefunction that extends beyond the negative ion " sphere " is taken into account, but this does not allow reductions as large as those found experimentally.

In the second approach, a reduction in central field potential is unnecessary and, for example, in $[\text{Ni}(\text{H}_2\text{O})_6]^{2+}$ all that has to be assumed (25) is that the electron spends about 10 per cent of the time delocalized on the ligands and this decreases the interelectronic repulsion energies nearly enough to account for what is observed. Such an interpretation allows α in the MO's given on page 29 to be given the value ~ 0.9, while the magnetic evidence suggests a figure more like 0.8.

It is possible that both of these processes take place to some degree, the former being somewhat more general and extensive than the latter, since MO formation requires very specific conditions of orbital availability from both a symmetry and an energetic point of view, and so might be expected to be less general in its operation.

Jorgensen has arranged ligands in the order in which such decreases in Racah parameters are observed, and has called it the nephelauxetic (cloud-expanding) series (26). Such a series does seem to be more in accord with what the chemist would intuitively feel is the capacity of the ligand to participate in covalent bond formation with the central metal than does the somewhat older spectrochemical series, but it would be dangerous to attempt to generalize too much on this matter.

(ii) Charge-Transfer Spectra

It is impossible to discuss charge-transfer spectra on other than an LF basis, since the basic notion is that an electron which is localized (or mainly so) in a ligand orbital can be excited to an orbital which is essentially localized on the central metal ion (or vice versa).

The oscillating electric dipole moment associated with electron transfer over such a distance is quite large and the transitions are, therefore, intense, having molar extinction coefficients ranging from ~2000–25,000 and higher (f's ~0.05–0.5). An example of such a transition (27) is given in Fig. 2.12 for $[Co(NH_3)_5Cl]^{2+}$, $[Co(NH_3)_5Br]^{2+}$, and $[Co(NH_3)_5I]^{2+}$.

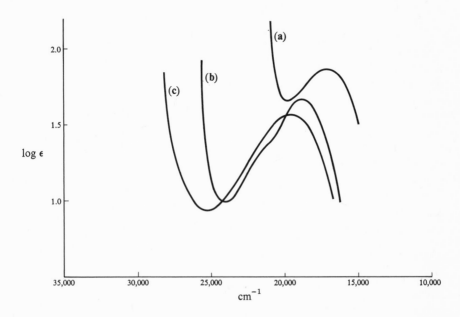

FIGURE 2.12.
charge transfer spectra of $[Co(NH_3)_5X]^{2+}$
(a) $X = I^-$
(b) $X = Br^-$
(c) $X = Cl^-$

These transitions are of the more common *reduction* type, i.e., the electron comes from the ligand to the metal, and it will be observed that there are two transitions. The lower frequency (and lower intensity) transition has been assigned as $e_g^* \leftarrow \pi$, i.e., one of the π electrons on the halogen has been excited to the "antibonding" e_g orbital of the central ion. This transition is relatively weak, because the overlap between the ligand π orbitals and the metal e_g orbitals is small and the molar extinction coefficient of this transition is only ~10–20. The higher-frequency transition has a molar extinction coefficient of ~18,000 and is assigned as $e_g^* \leftarrow \sigma$, i.e., a σ electron from the ligands being excited to the e_g^* orbital of the central ion. The overlap between these two orbitals is large and the intensity is correspondingly higher for this transition.

Such transitions are typical of the types of charge-transfer transitions encountered. It might be thought that the low-frequency transition is simply the triplet analogue of the more intense high-frequency transition; a useful guide here is that the extent to which the "triplet" transition is allowed depends upon the magnitude of the spin-orbit coupling constant and this is larger for iodine as compared with chlorine, by at least a factor of 20, whereas the intensities of the low-frequency bands hardly change. The assignment can, therefore, be rejected.

It is also possible to get two other types of charge-transfer transition. The first of these occurs when an electron from an anion which is *not* in the primary co-ordination sphere is excited to a molecular orbital of the complex. Such transitions are known and resemble the charge-transfer spectra in benzene-iodine mixtures. The second type occurs when the ligands are polyatomic, e.g., CNS^- or *o*-phenanthroline, when there are frequently intra-ligand charge transfer spectra. In CNS^- there is always a transition between $32-37,000 \text{ cm}^{-1}$ and in such cases it is advisable to know the spectrum of some compound involving the anion, but not in a complexed form (e.g., in the above case, KCNS).

Many other references to charge-transfer specta will be found in the various books and papers already cited.

B. TETRAHEDRAL COMPLEXES

(i) Crystal Field Transitions

Tetrahedral complexes have been treated separately from the octahedral complexes because of the less compelling nature of the assignments that have been made in the various cases. At the present time it can safely be said that only two tetrahedral complexes have had any of their transitions assigned with any certitude. The first one (*28, 29*) is the $[MnCl_4]^{2-}$ ion which has a d^5 configuration; the second is the 6300 cm^{-1} transition in $[CoCl_4]^{2-}$ which has been analyzed (*30*) as $^4T_1 \leftarrow {}^4A_2$ with a considerable spin-orbit splitting of the crystal field levels, together with some degree of tetragonal distortion (in the compound Cs_3CoCl_5). The spectrum of $[MnCl_4]^{2-}$ is reproduced in Fig. 2.13 and its resemblance to the octahedral Mn^{2+} spectrum can easily be seen. The differences are that there has been a very large decrease in the interterm separation, $^4G-{}^6S$, as is shown by the frequency at which the "sharp" transition to the $^4A_1$ level occurs ($22,450 \text{ cm}^{-1}$ in the tetrahedral complex as compared with $\sim 25,000 \text{ cm}^{-1}$ in the octahedral hydrate, i.e., a 16 per cent reduction as compared with about 7 per cent for the octahedral). There is also an increase in intensity of the second band ($^4T_{2g}(G) \leftarrow {}^6A_{1g}$ in the octahedral complex—$^4T_2 \leftarrow {}^6A_1$ in the tetrahedral) relative to both the first band and the "sharp" group. The reason for the intensification is clear, since the $^4T_2 \leftarrow {}^6A_1$ transition in a tetrahedron is fully allowed electronically, whereas it is only vibronically allowed in the octahedron.

The exact assignments for the rest of the spectrum are not quite so clear, but at least the lower-frequency group behaves much as expected. Note also that the tetrahedral and octahedral Orgel diagrams are identical for the d^5 configuration, since a change in the sign of D only affects the off-diagonal matrix elements in the perturbation secular determinants, and since the latter are symmetric, then only $(Dq)^2$ terms appear in the energy expression. The diagram is, therefore, unchanged as compared with the octahedral one, except that the appropriate value of Dq for the tetrahedral complex is much smaller than for the octahedral complexes.

It is not possible to compare octahedral and tetrahedral complexes having the same ligand (and even then there is no guarantee that the internuclear distances

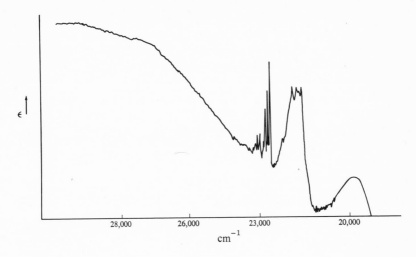

FIGURE 2.13.
spectrum of $Cs_2 MnCl_4$ solid, i.e., $[MnCl_4]^{2-}$

would be identical), so it is not possible to give an exact answer as to whether the tetrahedral Dq value is $4/9$ of the octahedral value. However, a large series of octahedral complexes seem to show that Cl^- is about 75 per cent as strong a perturbing ligand as H_2O. It is found that a Dq value of ~ 790 cm^{-1} is best for the $[Mn(H_2O)_6]^{2+}$ spectrum and ~ 265 cm^{-1} for the $[MnCl_4]^{2-}$ spectrum (28). Since 75 per cent of $4/9 \equiv 1/3$ it will be seen that the value obtained to compare with the tetrahedral Dq value is very close indeed (263 cm^{-1}!). It would thus seem that, in the main, the CF approximation can usefully be applied to tetrahedral complexes.

There are, as yet however, many unexplained features of the spectra of such complexes as $[CoCl_4]^{2-}$, $[NiCl_4]^{2-}$, and $[CuCl_4]^{2-}$, not to mention the spectra obtained by preparing single crystals of ZnO, which has tetrahedral sites, doped with these metals. It seems clear that there are at least two other complicating factors in these spectra—spin-orbit coupling and nuclear distortion—and the complete treatment of these effects is beyond the scope of this discussion.

(ii) Charge-Transfer Spectra

Charge-transfer spectra constitute a very important and separate group of spectra, including as they do the spectra of such well known anions as CrO_4^{2-}, ClO_4^-, MnO_4^-, MnO_4^{2-}, SO_4^{2-}, and many others. All of the anions listed, with the exception of MnO_4^{2-}, have d^0 ground-state configurations and the only transitions are, therefore, of the charge-transfer type. There has been a great deal of activity in the past two or three years with regard to these spectra, and the assignments now appear to be more likely correct than earlier attempts. Two typical examples will be discussed, $[MnO_4]^-$ and $[MnO_4]^{2-}$, d^0 and d^1.

The permanganate ion has two main absorption systems at $\sim 18,000$ cm^{-1} and 32,000 cm^{-1}. The first of these has been assigned (31, 32, 33) configurationally as $e^*(\pi)^* \leftarrow t_1(n)$, i.e., a transition of an electron in a completely non-bonding ligand orbital to the antibonding $e^*(\pi)$ orbital. This transition shows a reasonable amount of vibrational structure; this is in accord with the nature of the orbitals involved, since the effect of such a transition on the force constants of the molecule is relatively small.

The transition at 32,000 cm^{-1} seems best assigned (31, 32) as a $t_2^* \leftarrow t_1$ excitation. This transition also shows some vibrational structure, although, in solution, this is not as marked as for the 18,000 cm^{-1} transition. It should be noted that both the $e^* \leftarrow t_1$ and $t_2^* \leftarrow t_1$ excitations are degenerate, the first giving rise to four possible upper states, $^{1,3}T_1$ and $^{1,3}T_2$, and the second to eight possible upper states, $^{1,3}A_2$, $^{1,3}E$, $^{1,3}T_1$, and $^{1,3}T_2$. The intensity ($\varepsilon_{max} \sim 2300$ for the first and ~ 2000 for the second) suggests that the $^1T_2 \leftarrow {}^1A_1$ component is the one which appears—since it is the electric dipole-allowed one. The transition at 32,000 cm^{-1} has the appearance of two overlapping transitions, but it is difficult to be certain of this. If this doubling were to be taken as real, then the frequencies would be $\sim 27,800$ cm^{-1} (3600 Å) and 32,000 cm^{-1} (3125 Å), and only the latter shows vibrational structure. There is also a weak transition on the low-frequency side of the 18,000 cm^{-1} band, but no evidence is available as to its possible assignment apart from the obvious identification as the triplet analogue of the stronger nearby system.

Manganate ion has a single "d" electron, in the e^* shell presumably, so the lowest-frequency transition could be, configurationally, either $t_2^* \leftarrow e^*$ or $e^* \leftarrow t_1$, with the former being favored (31, 32). The ion shows four bands, at $\sim 16,500$ cm^{-1} (6050 Å), $\sim 23,000$ cm^{-1} (4350 Å), 28,000 cm^{-1} (3575 Å), and 33,400 cm^{-1} (3000 Å). The highest-frequency band is most likely to be assigned as the analogue of the 32,000 cm^{-1} band of $[MnO_4]^-$, i.e., $t_2^* \leftarrow t_1$ on the basis of analogy, but the systems have not, as yet, been assigned beyond reasonable doubt. The two other bands are probably related to the $e^* \leftarrow t_1$ excitation, but this is almost pure speculation.

From what has been said, it is clear enough that the charge-transfer spectra of the tetrahedral oxyanion species are far from assigned, although there are some grounds for thinking that the final results will not be too far different from the tentative outline given above.

C. MORE COMPLICATED SPECTRA

It is not intended to discuss the more complicated spectra in detail, but simply to point out what further complications are likely to be encountered.

(i) Nuclear Distortions from Cubic Symmetry

Very few complex ions are, in fact, perfectly octahedral or tetrahedral, as far as is known from the evidence. For this reason many of the degenerate levels will split even further if the symmetry is reduced. Thus, the spectra of square-planar complexes are more complicated, because of the large number of excited levels which exist and crude theory cannot provide enough information to enable the transitions to be assigned with any certainty. Included under this heading are the Jahn–Teller distortions, which may have profound spectroscopic consequences (4, 34), but these are beyond the scope of the present discussion.

(ii) The Effects of Spin-Orbit Coupling

As the atomic number of the central ion increases, so the coupling between spin and orbital angular momenta increases and gives energy-level diagrams (35) very different from those calculated without taking this effect into account. When the spin-orbit coupling and the crystal field are of roughly the same magnitude, identification becomes very difficult, but some attempts have been made to discuss these spectra. The original references should be consulted for such discussion (35, 36, 37).

(iii) Solvation and Lattice Effects

It is frequently not valid to assume that spectra taken either in solution or in a solid are necessarily those of the species that was dissolved or crystallized (or occluded). A substantial body of evidence (38, 39) shows that both these effects can be very important, and so it is desirable that the species in question be positively identified before any attempt is made to assign the spectrum.

In the spectroscopy of organic compounds in solution, it is difficult enough to assign the spectra even when the structure of the absorbing molecule is beyond doubt. The inorganic chemist is all too frequently in the position of not knowing for sure what the absorbing species is, because of the much higher solvation energies and lattice energies associated with these processes in inorganic chemistry; he must, therefore, be correspondingly wary.

REFERENCES

1. F. A. Cotton, *Chemical Applications of Group Theory*, Interscience, New York, 1963.
2. J. H. Van Vleck, *J. Phys. Chem.* **41**: 67 (1937).
3. A. D. Liehr, *Prog. Inorg. Chem.* **3**: 281 (1962).
4. T. M. Dunn, "The Visible and Ultra-violet Spectra of Complex Compounds," in J. Lewis and R. Wilkins (eds.), *Modern Coordination Chemistry*, Interscience, New York, 1960, chap. IV.
5. F. A. Cotton and M. D. Meyers, *J. Chem. Soc.* **82**: 5023 (1960).
6. T. Dreisch and O. Kallscheuer, *Z. Physik. Chem.* **B45**: 19 (1939).
7. O. G. Holmes and D. S. McClure, *J. Chem. Phys.* **26**: 1686 (1957).
8. B. N. Figgis and J. Lewis, "The Magnetochemistry of Complex Compounds," in J. Lewis and R. Wilkins (eds.), *Modern Coordination Chemistry*, Interscience, New York, 1960, chap. VI.
9. F. E. Ilse and H. Hartmann, *Z. Naturforsch.* **6a**: 751 (1951).
10. L. E. Orgel, *J. Chem. Phys.* **23**: 1004 (1955).
11. J. Ferguson, *J. Chem. Phys.* **32**: 537 (1960).
12. R. I. Colmar and F. W. Schwartz, *J. Am. Chem. Soc.* **54**: 3204 (1932).
13. D. S. McClure, *Solid State Phys.* **9**: 400 (1959).
14. O. Bostrup and C. K. Jorgensen, *Acta Chem. Scand.* **11**: 4223 (1957).
15. T. Dreisch and W. Trommer, *Z. Physik. Chem.* **B37**: 37 (1957).
16. C. K. Jorgensen, *Acta Chem. Scand.* **9**: 1362 (1955).
17. T. M. Dunn, *J. Appl. Chem.* **6**: 1 (1963).
18. L. E. Orgel, *J. Chem. Phys.* **23**: 1824 (1955).
19. C. K. Jorgensen, *Acta Chem. Scand.* **11**: 53 (1957).
20. L. J. Heidt, G. F. Koster and A. M. Johnson, *J. Am. Chem. Soc.* **80**: 6471 (1959).
21. C. K. Jorgensen, in *Inst. Intern. de Chim. Solvay, 10ᵉ Conseil de Chim.* (Brussels) 1956, p. 355.
22. C. K. Jorgensen, *Absorption Spectra and Chemical Bonding in Complexes*, Pergamon Press, Oxford, 1962.
23. C. J. Ballhausen, *Introduction to Ligand Field Theory*, McGraw-Hill, New York, 1962.
24. J. S. Griffith, *The Theory of Transition Metal Ions*, Cambridge Univ. Press, Cambridge, 1961.
25. J. Owen, *Proc. Roy. Soc.* **A227**: 183 (1955).
26. C. K. Jorgensen, *Discussions Faraday Soc.* **[26]**: 110 (1958).
27. M. Linhard and M. Weigel, *Z. Anorg. Chem.* **266**: 49 (1951).
28. S. Buffagni and T. M. Dunn, *Nature* **188**: 937 (1960).
29. A Furlani and C. Furlani, *J. Inorg. Nucl. Chem.* **19**: 51 (1961).
30. R. J. Clark, T. M. Dunn, and C. F. Stoneman, unpublished research.
31. M. C. R. Symons, "Advances in the Chemistry of Coordination Compounds," in S. Kirschner (ed.), *Proceedings of the VIth International Conference on Coordination Chemistry*, Macmillan, New York, 1961.
32. A. Carrington and C. K. Jorgensen, *Mol. Phys.* **4**: 395 (1961).
33. C. J. Ballhausen and A. D. Liehr, *Mol. Spectr.* **2**: 342 (1958).

34. A. D. Liehr, *Prog. Inorg. Chem.* **3**: 281 (1962).
35. A. D. Liehr and C. J. Ballhausen, *Ann. Phys.* (N.Y.) **6**: 136 (1959).
36. L. E. Orgel, *J. Chem. Soc.* **1952**: 4756.
37. C. K. Jorgensen, *Acta Chem. Scand.* **10**: 887 (1956).
38. L. Katzin and Gebert, *J. Am. Chem. Soc.* **72**: 5464 (1950).
39. S. Buffagni and T. M. Dunn, *J. Chem. Soc.* **1961**: 5105.

CHAPTER 3 THE MAGNETISM OF INORGANIC COMPLEXES

THOMAS M. DUNN

A. INTRODUCTION

The magnetic behavior of inorganic ions and complexes can be divided into four main classes, as shown in Table 3.1. Only paramagnetism will be discussed in this section.

TABLE 3.1.

Type of Magnetism	χ (Susceptibility) Cgs	Dependence on H
diamagnetism	$\sim 10^{-6}$	independent
paramagnetism	$\sim 100 \times 10^{-6}$	independent
ferromagnetism	$\sim 10^{-2} - 10^{+4}$	independent
antiferromagnetism	$\sim 1 - 100 \times 10^{-6}$	sometimes dependent

The bulk susceptibilities are usually characterized by the magnitude of the magnetic susceptibility (molar, specific, or volume)

K (volume susceptibility) $= I/H$ where $I =$ intensity of magnetization, i.e., the degree of magnetic dipole alignment and $H =$ field strength (applied)

or

$$\chi \text{ (specific susceptibility)} = \frac{K}{\rho}, \rho = \text{density}$$

and

$\chi_{M \text{ or } A} = \chi \times$ molecular or atomic weight (χ_M is called the molar susceptibility)

To explain the relationship between χ_M and the magnetic moment it is, perhaps, advisable to briefly review the topic of the behavior of a single unpaired electron having no orbital angular momentum (say, an s electron). Such an electron has a spin quantum number $S = s = 1/2$, and the spin degeneracy is $2S + 1 = 2$. In the presence of a magnetic field this twofold degenerate level is split into two nondegenerate component levels, the splitting magnitude ΔE being given by

$$\Delta E = g\beta H$$

where g is the Landé g factor or "spectroscopic splitting factor" and for field-free ions, assuming Russell–Saunders coupling (3),

$$g = 1 + \frac{J(J + 1) - L(L + 1) + S(S + 1)}{2J(J + 1)}$$

β is the unit magnetic moment, i.e., the Bohr magneton, and $\beta = e\hbar/2mc$. H is the magnetic field.

For a single electron with $L = 0$ and $S = 1/2$, $g = 2$, as can be verified from the formula (since $J = 1/2$), and for the usual strength magnetic fields applied, the splitting amounts to 1–2 cm^{-1}. At room temperature ($kT \sim 200$ cm^{-1}) the two levels will both be populated, with somewhat fewer electrons being in the upper state than the lower. Since these two levels correspond to the electron having its magnetic moment aligned parallel with the field and opposed to the field for the lower and upper levels respectively, there is now an average magnetic moment of the assembly of electrons. (And since these electrons are usually bound to an atom, the collection of atoms has become "magnetically polarized.")

The total magnetic moment P is dependent upon the way in which the electrons are distributed over the stationary-state levels, assuming Boltzmann's distribution and (2)

$$P = N \frac{\sum\limits_{n,m} \mu_{n,m} e^{-E_m/kT}}{\sum e^{-E_m/kT}}$$

where $\mu_{n,m}$ are the magnetic moments in the states n and m respectively, and E_m is the energy of the atom ion or molecule in the field. Van Vleck has shown that such a formulation, upon expanding the energy as a power series in the magnetic field, and assuming that $kT \gg \Delta E$ (ΔE being the total separation between levels), leads to

$$\chi_i = N \left[\sum_{n,m} \frac{[E_{o,m}^{(1)}]^2}{j_m kT} - 2 \sum_{n,m} \frac{E_{o,m}^{(2)}}{j_m} \right]$$

where
$$E_{o,m}^{(1)} = \langle \phi_{o,m} | \mu_i | \phi_{o,m} \rangle$$

$$E_{o,m}^{(2)} = \sum_{n,m} \frac{|\langle \phi_{o,m} | \mu_i | \phi_{n,m} \rangle|^2}{E_o - E_n}$$

and
$$\mu_i = (L + 2S)\beta.$$

For an atom or ion having a total electronic angular momentum denoted by J, it is possible to show that (2, 3, 4)

$$\chi_A = \frac{\mathcal{N} g^2 J(J + 1)\beta^2}{3kT}$$

provided $\beta H/kT \ll 1$, where $\mathcal{N}$ is Avogadro's number, k is the Boltzmann constant, T is the absolute temperature, β is as defined above, g is the Landé spectroscopic splitting factor, and H is the applied magnetic field. This equation clearly shows the basis of the Curie Law, in that $\chi \propto 1/T$ and if the "effective magneton number" is defined as

$$\mu_{\text{eff}} = g\sqrt{J(J + 1)}$$

then it is clear that

$$\chi = \frac{\mathcal{N} \beta^2}{3kT} \mu_{\text{eff}}^2$$

This formulation affords the means of obtaining information about the J value of the lowest component of the ground term of an ion, but seldom do the "ions" in a complex give a value in accord with what is expected theoretically. Instead, it is more frequently found in the first transition series of metal complexes that the magnetic moments are close to the so-called "spin-only" magnetic moments (5, 6), i.e., that

$$\mu_{\text{eff}} \sim \sqrt{4S(S + 1)}, \text{ i.e., } \mu_{\text{eff}} = 2\sqrt{S(S + 1)} = g\sqrt{S(S + 1)}$$

The experimental values of the susceptibility do not agree precisely with the values of μ_{eff} calculated from such a simple formula. It was, in fact, shown as early as 1932 (7) that the main reason why the formula is even roughly applicable is that the orbital contribution to the total electronic angular momentum (J) is quenched by the perturbing effects of "crystalline fields." Since the magnetic moment of the free-ion level with wave function ϕ_j depends upon both contributions, i.e.,

$$\mu_i = \int \phi_j^* L_{(i} + 2S_i)\phi_j \, dt = \langle \phi_j | L_i + 2S_i | \phi_j \rangle$$

and the "freezing out" of the orbital part leads, for the most part, to the reduced moments which are found experimentally. The values do not, however, always equal the "spin-only" value, being sometimes too large and sometimes too small (5, 6). It is with these problems that modern magnetochemistry (5, 6) concerns itself, using the magnitude of the departures from free-ion moments to infer the stereochemistry of the compound concerned.

As was remarked earlier (p. 34, Chapter 1), the most profound effects on the magnetic moment are caused by the reduction of the maximum permissible value of the spin of quantum number from 5/2 to 3/2 when a strong cubic field is applied to the ion and the d_ε and d_γ sets of orbitals split so far apart that the d_ε fills first and interactions between them can be ignored. This limit forms the basis for the Van Vleck (8)–Kotani (9) model of magnetism in complexes (10, 11), to be outlined below.

B. THE VAN VLECK–KOTANI MODEL

(i) d_ε^1, d_ε^5 Configurations (i.e., t_{2g}^1, t_{2g}^5)

Suppose that a strong octahedral field perturbs an ion such as Ti^{3+}, having a single d electron. As outlined in Chapter 1, the ^2D term of the free ion splits to give a $^2T_{2g}$ term depressed by $4Dq$ and a ^2E_g term raised by $6Dq$. Suppose, in addition, that Dq is very large, large enough in fact, so that if four electrons are added (for an ion such as Mn^{3+}), they would all go into the lower of the two levels, i.e., all into the d_ε level. The case under consideration is that of Ti^{3+} in which only a single electron is added, but the splitting is imagined to be large. This has no consequences for d^1 but the effects will become apparent when the configuration d^2 is considered.

The $^2T_{2g}$ term is sixfold degenerate (3 orbit × 2 spin) but there are only *two* actual energy levels, since $J_{\text{eff}} = L_{\text{eff}} + S$ and $L_{\text{eff}} - S$. Using the three orbital wavefunctions derived in Chapter 1 for the d_ε levels, the six wavefunctions, including spin, can be constructed (3); α refers to spin $+1/2$ and β to spin $-1/2$. Let these wavefunctions be labelled according to Table 3.2.

TABLE 3.2.

$\langle\phi_i|$	d_ε Wavefunctions (including spin)	$M_{L_{\text{eff}}}$
$\langle\phi_1|$	$1/\sqrt{2}\,[\langle 2| - \langle\bar{2}|]\alpha$	0
$\langle\phi_2|$	$1/\sqrt{2}\,[\langle 2| - \langle\bar{2}|]\beta$	0
$\langle\phi_3|$	$\langle 1|\alpha$	1
$\langle\phi_4|$	$\langle 1|\beta$	1
$\langle\phi_5|$	$\langle\bar{1}|\alpha$	-1
$\langle\phi_6|$	$\langle\bar{1}|\beta$	-1

The first thing that must be done is to calculate the effect of the spin-orbit coupling, since the splittings produced by the magnetic field are only ~ 1 cm^{-1}, whereas the splittings brought about by spin-orbit coupling vary in the first transition row from ~ 100 cm^{-1} for Ti$^+$ to ~ 1000 cm^{-1} for Cu^{2+}.

The spin-orbit interaction operator is (*1, 12, 13*)

$$H' = \sum_i \frac{1}{2m^2c^2}\left(\frac{1}{r_i}\frac{\partial V(r_i)}{\partial r}\right) \boldsymbol{L \cdot S} = \lambda \boldsymbol{L \cdot S}$$

and

$$\boldsymbol{L \cdot S} = \tfrac{1}{2}(L_x + iL_y)(S_x - iS_y) + \tfrac{1}{2}(L_x - iL_y)(S_x + iS_y) + L_z S_z$$

The first-order correction to the energy is, as usual, $\langle \phi_j | H' | \phi_j \rangle$. As an example, consider $\langle \phi_1 | H' | \phi_1 \rangle$.

The only part of the problem which has to be calculated is the $\langle \phi_1 | \boldsymbol{L \cdot S} | \phi_1 \rangle$ component since the rest is expressed parametrically in terms of the term spin-orbit coupling constant, λ. The expanded form of $\boldsymbol{L \cdot S}$ in terms of $(L_x \pm iL_y)$, etc., is very useful, since these operators ("ladder" or "up and down" operators as they are called) simply raise or lower the quantum number $m \equiv m_l$ by unity (or change the spin quantum number from $+1/2$ to $-1/2$ or vice versa) or else they yield zero. For example, $(L_x + iL_y)$ operating upon $|m\rangle$ yields $|m + 1\rangle$ if such a value exists and zero otherwise, i.e., if the set of m values runs from $2, 1 \ldots \bar{2}$, then only

$$|(L_x + iL_y)|\bar{2}\rangle$$

$$|\bar{1}\rangle$$

$$|0\rangle$$

$$|1\rangle$$

are nonzero. Similarly for $(L_x - iL_y)$, except that this operator lowers the value of m by unity. For a detailed treatment of these operators one of the texts on atomic structure should be consulted (e.g., *1, 13, 14*). Thus

$$(L_x + iL_y)|n, l, m, s\rangle = \hbar[l(l + 1) - m(m + 1)]^{\frac{1}{2}} \cdot |n, l, m + 1, s\rangle$$

$(L_x + iL_y)|m\rangle$ is nonzero only for $m = 1, 0, \bar{1}, \bar{2}$

$(L_x - iL_y)|m\rangle$ is nonzero only for $m = 2, 1, 0, \bar{1}$

$L_z|m\rangle$ is nonzero only for $m = 2, 1, \bar{1}, \bar{2}$

$(S_x + iS_y)|s\rangle$ is nonzero only for $s = -\frac{1}{2}$, i.e., β

$(S_x - iS_y)|s\rangle$ is nonzero only for $s = +\frac{1}{2}$, i.e., α

$S_z|s\rangle$ is nonzero only for $s = +\frac{1}{2}$ or $-\frac{1}{2}$

$$\boldsymbol{L \cdot S}|\phi_1\rangle = \tfrac{1}{2}(L_x + iL_y)(S_x - iS_y)|\phi_1\rangle + \tfrac{1}{2}(L_x - iL_y)(S_x + iS_y)|\phi_1\rangle + L_z S_z|\phi_1\rangle$$

and only the first term is nonzero [since, for the second term $(S_x + iS_y)|\phi_1\rangle = 0$ because $(S_x + iS_y)|\alpha\rangle = 0$, and for the final term ϕ_1 has $M_{L\ \text{eff}} = 0$, i.e., $L_z|\phi_1\rangle = 0$.]

From the above discussion

$$(S_x - iS_y)|\phi_1\rangle = \frac{1}{\sqrt{2}}[|2\rangle - |\bar{2}\rangle]\beta$$

that is,

$$L \cdot S|\phi_1\rangle = \frac{1}{2\sqrt{2}}\{(L_x + iL_y)|2\rangle - (L_x + iL_y)|\bar{2}\rangle\}\beta$$

$$= \frac{1}{2\sqrt{2}}\{0 - (6 - 2)^{\frac{1}{2}}\bar{1}|\rangle\}\beta$$

$$= \frac{-1}{\sqrt{2}}|\bar{1}\rangle\beta$$

$$= \frac{-1}{\sqrt{2}}\phi_6$$

Similarly,

$$L \cdot S|\phi_2\rangle = \frac{1}{\sqrt{2}}|\phi_3\rangle$$

$$L \cdot S|\phi_3\rangle = |2\rangle\beta + \frac{1}{2}|\phi_3\rangle$$

$$L \cdot S|\phi_4\rangle = \frac{-1}{2}|\phi_4\rangle$$

$$L \cdot S|\phi_5\rangle = \frac{-1}{2}|\phi_5\rangle$$

$$L \cdot S|\phi_6\rangle = |\bar{2}\rangle\alpha + \frac{1}{2}|\phi_6\rangle$$

Thus, $\langle\phi_1|L \cdot S|\phi_1\rangle = 0$, since ϕ_1 and ϕ_6 are orthogonal, and $\langle\phi_6|L \cdot S|\phi_1\rangle = -1/\sqrt{2}$, since the ϕ_j are normalized to unity. The complete perturbation secular determinant is, therefore,

$$
\begin{vmatrix}
 & \phi_1 & \phi_2 & \phi_3 & \phi_4 & \phi_5 & \phi_6 \\
\phi_1 & -E & & & & & \frac{-1}{\sqrt{2}} \\
\phi_2 & & -E & \frac{1}{\sqrt{2}} & & & \\
\phi_3 & & \frac{1}{\sqrt{2}} & \frac{1}{2}-E & & & \\
\phi_4 & & & & -\frac{1}{2}-E & & \\
\phi_5 & & & & & -\frac{1}{2}-E & \\
\phi_6 & \frac{-1}{\sqrt{2}} & & & & & +\frac{1}{2}-E
\end{vmatrix} = 0
$$

where the energies are in units of λ, the free-ion ground *term* spin-orbit coupling parameter ($\lambda = \pm \zeta/2S$, where ζ is the one-electron coupling parameter and S is the total spin quantum number.

This determinant can clearly be rearranged and simplified to give two quadratic equations and two linear equations, and the solutions and wavefunctions are as follows:

$$E = +\lambda \text{ (twofold degenerate)} \quad \psi_1 = \frac{1}{\sqrt{3}}[\phi_2 - \sqrt{2}\phi_3]$$

$$\psi_2 = \frac{1}{\sqrt{3}}[\phi_1 - \sqrt{2}\phi_6]$$

$$E = -\frac{1}{2}\lambda \text{ (fourfold degenerate)} \quad \psi_3 = \frac{1}{\sqrt{3}}[\sqrt{2}\phi_2 - \phi_3]$$

$$\psi_4 = \frac{1}{\sqrt{3}}[\sqrt{2}\phi_1 + \phi_6]$$

$$\psi_5 = \phi_4$$

$$\psi_6 = \phi_5$$

It is now possible to calculate the magnetic moment of an electron in the d_ε group of levels including spin-orbit interaction, since

$$\mu = \langle \psi_j | L_z + 2S_z | \psi_j \rangle \beta$$

It is at once clear that neither ψ_5 nor ψ_6 have any first- or second-order Zeeman effect, i.e., the levels are not split by a magnetic field and the magnetic moment arising from them is therefore zero. This occurs since $\psi_5 \equiv \phi_4$ and $\psi_6 = \phi_5$, the former having spin β and the latter spin α; also, ϕ_4 has $M_L = +1$ and ϕ_5 has $M_L = -1$, so that even in case of a small energy difference between the levels the contributions to the moment from spin and orbit are exactly opposite.

$$\frac{\mu}{\beta H} = \langle \psi_5 | L_z + 2S_z | \psi_5 \rangle = \langle \psi_6 | L_z + 2S_z | \psi_6 \rangle = 0$$

By applying the same methods as before it is easy to show that

$$(L_z + 2S_z)|\psi_1\rangle = \sqrt{6}|\phi_3\rangle - |\psi_1\rangle$$

$$|\psi_2\rangle = \sqrt{6}|\phi_6\rangle + |\psi_2\rangle$$

$$|\psi_3\rangle = -\sqrt{3}|\phi_3\rangle - |\psi_3\rangle$$

$$|\psi_4\rangle = -\sqrt{3}|\phi_6\rangle + |\psi_4\rangle$$

Calculation of the complete matrix yields the following results:

$$\langle\psi_1|\mu|\psi_1\rangle = +\beta H$$
$$\langle\psi_2|\mu|\psi_2\rangle = -\beta H$$
$$\langle\psi_1|\mu|\psi_2\rangle = 0 = \langle\psi_2|\mu|\psi_1\rangle$$
$$\langle\psi_3|\mu|\psi_3\rangle = 0 = \langle\psi_4|\mu|\psi_4\rangle$$
$$\langle\psi_3|\mu|\psi_4\rangle = 0 = \langle\psi_4|\mu|\psi_3\rangle$$

That is, the pair of levels at $+\lambda$ are split in first order by $2\beta H$, whereas the fourfold degenerate levels at $-\lambda/2$ are unaffected, in first order, by the magnetic field. The presence of the magnetic field, however, mixes the pair of levels at $+\lambda$ with two of the four levels at $-\lambda/2$, thus removing the complete degeneracy of the lower four levels. The magnitude of the energy shift is $H_{ij}^2/\pm 3/2\,\lambda$, where $H_{ij} = \sqrt{2}\beta H$, bearing in mind that for the upper pair of levels the denominator is $+3/2\lambda$ and is $-3/2\,\lambda$ for the lower pair (which are ψ_3, ψ_4 since ψ_5, ψ_6 do not have any first- or second-order Zeeman effect).

The final diagram for the energy levels is shown in Fig. 3.1. These energy values can be substituted into the formula for the susceptibility (not discussed here!) and the expression becomes, upon refinement (9)

$$\chi = \frac{\mathscr{N}\beta^2}{3kT}\left[\frac{8 + (3x - 8)e^{-3x/2}}{x(2 + e^{-3x/2})}\right]$$

where $x = \lambda/kT$. Comparison with the earlier equation for χ in terms of μ_{eff} yields

$$\mu_{\text{eff}} = \sqrt{\frac{8 + (3x - 8)e^{-3x/2}}{x(2 + e^{-3x/2})}} \cdot \beta$$

This is frequently expressed in terms of the "effective *number* of Bohr magnetons, n_{eff}," i.e.

$$n_{\text{eff}} = \frac{\mu_{\text{eff}}}{\beta}$$

or

$$n_{\text{eff}}(d_\varepsilon^1) = \sqrt{\frac{8 + (3x - 8)e^{-3x/2}}{x(2 + e^{-3x/2})}}$$

The exact behavior of such a complex function with respect to changes in temperature (9, 10, 13) is not immediately obvious, and is shown in Fig. 3.2, but the limiting values are $n_{\text{eff}} \to 0$ as $T \to 0$ and $n_{\text{eff}} \to \sqrt{5}$ (from below) as $T \to \infty$. These limiting values arise in the case $T \to 0$, from the fact that at such a temperature, only the lowest doubly degenerate levels are occupied and these have no first-order Zeeman effect, i.e., the spin and orbital motions generate magnetic fields which oppose each other and the resultant level is thus nonmagnetic. The value of $\sqrt{5}$ is what is to be expected for a free-ion p electron with no spin-orbit

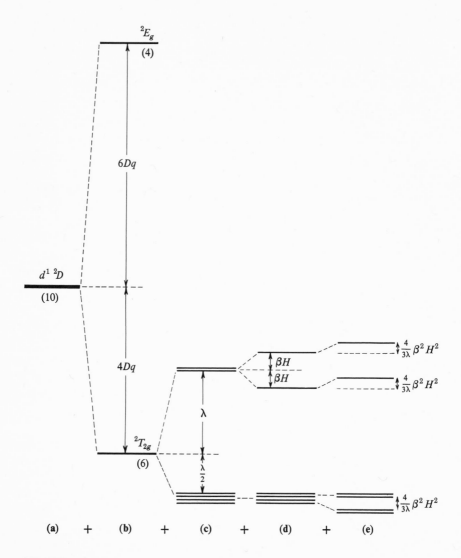

FIGURE 3.1.
  (a) field-free ion term
  (b) octahedral CF
  (c) spin-orbit coupling
  (d) magnetic field
  (e) second-order Zeeman effect

coupling, i.e., $\sqrt{4S(S+1) + L(L+1)}$. This value suggests that the d_ε level behaves like a p level if the temperature is high enough to ignore the effects of spin-orbit coupling, i.e., as $kT/\lambda \to \infty$. That this isomorphism is real has been adequately demonstrated (13).

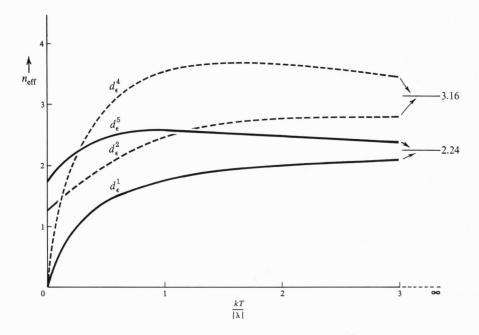

FIGURE 3.2.

The d_ε^5 configuration is of much greater interest from the experimental side since $K_4Fe(CN)_6$ has this configuration and it becomes possible to compare theoretical and experimental results. Since the d_ε^5 configuration has a nearly closed shell (d_ε^6), i.e., d_ε^{6-1}, then the previous calculations are valid, with the proviso that the diagram must be inverted, since the sign of λ changes for terms arising from configurations that are more than half filled. (This inversion does not apply to the octahedral field effect but to the spin-orbit coupling, this being sufficient to invert the whole pattern.) Replacing x in the previous equation for the susceptibility of d_ε^1 by $-x$ yields (3, 9, 10, 13)

$$n_{\text{eff}}(d_\varepsilon^5) = \frac{3x + 8(1 - e^{-3/2x})}{x(1 + 2e^{-3/2x})}$$

The behavior of this function is somewhat different from that of the d_ε^1 function, with temperature. For $T \to 0$, $n_{\text{eff}} \to \sqrt{3}$ and for $T \to \infty$ (i.e., as $kT/\lambda \to \infty$), $n_{\text{eff}} \to \sqrt{5}$ as previously, but from above (see Fig. 3.2).

The physical significance of this curve is that at low temperatures only the very lowest level will be occupied (that denoted ψ_1 in the calculation) and this has no orbital contribution, i.e., n_{eff} will be that for a single electron spin, $\sqrt{4S(S+1)} \equiv \sqrt{3}$, whereas if the temperature rise is such that the levels at $-\lambda + \beta H(\psi_2)$ and $+\lambda/2$ (ψ_5 and ψ_6) are populated, then there is a contribution to the moment from the orbital motion; this will start to decrease as the highest doubly degenerate nonmagnetic level (ψ_3 and ψ_4) is also populated. Once the temperature is large enough so that $kT \gg 3/2\ \lambda$ the moment will converge *from above* to the value $\sqrt{5}$ for the same reasons outlined for d_ε^1. It must be borne in mind also that the behavior of $\mu_{\text{eff}}(n_{\text{eff}})$ with temperature depends upon the (assumed) crystal perturbation being perfectly octahedral. Deviations of this symmetry have been discussed in the literature (*15, 16, 17*) and will not be pursued here.

(ii) d_γ^1, d_γ^3 Configurations (i.e., e_g^1)

This configuration is magnetically trivial, as can readily be seen. Let

$$\langle\phi_1| = \frac{1}{\sqrt{2}}\,[\langle 2| - \langle \bar{2}|]\alpha$$

$$\langle\phi_2| = \frac{1}{\sqrt{2}}\,[\langle 2| - \langle \bar{2}|]\beta$$

$$\langle\phi_3| = \langle 0|\alpha$$

$$\langle\phi_4| = \langle 0|\beta$$

$L_z|\phi_i\rangle = 0$ for $i = 1, 2, 3, 4$ and $(L_x \pm iL_y)|\phi_i\rangle$ is also zero, since the ladder operators cannot transform the ϕ_i into any other member of the set. There is, thus, no spin-orbit splitting for the d_γ^n configurations. Magnetically, ϕ_1 and ϕ_3 are eigenfunctions of S_z with eigenvalues $+1/2$ and $-1/2$ respectively so that

$$\langle\phi_1|L_z + 2S_z|\phi_1\rangle = +\beta H$$

$$\langle\phi_2|L_z + 2S_z|\phi_2\rangle = -\beta H$$

and there are no second-order terms. The susceptibility χ is, therefore, exactly the same as for a single electron in an orbit having no orbital angular momentum.

$$\chi = \frac{\mathcal{N}\beta^2}{3kT}\cdot g^2 \cdot S(S+1)$$

$$= \frac{\mathcal{N}\beta^2}{3kT}\cdot 2^2 \cdot \frac{3}{4}$$

$$= \frac{\mathcal{N}\beta^2}{kT}$$

and $\mu_{\text{eff}} = \sqrt{3}\beta$. Thus, the configuration is magnetically simple.

(iii) d_ε^2, d_ε^4 Configurations

Once the methods for treating the d_ε^1 configuration have been understood, there is little difficulty in extending the treatment to d_ε^2 and d_ε^4, except for the necessity of using determinantal wavefunctions for the two-electron problem.

The lowest term of the d_ε^2 configuration in an octahedral field has threefold orbital and spin degeneracy. Thus, the configuration is ninefold degenerate, including spin, if only the highest spin multiplicity terms are considered.

The first step is to construct a basic set of wavefunctions χ_i for the triplet levels; this is done in the same way as was described in Chapter 1 (p. 18) for setting up the wavefunctions for the ^3F and ^3P terms of an atom or ion. The wavefunctions must be constructed so that they have all possible permutations of the $M_{L\,\mathrm{eff}}$ and M_S values; i.e., since the d_ε shell behaves like a p shell, the former are $1, 0, \bar{1}$ and the latter also $1, 0, \bar{1}$. The six functions having $M_S \neq 0$ are easy to construct, whereas those with $M_S = 0$ are linear combinations of two indistinguishable assignments of spins, e.g., χ_8 has $M_L = \bar{1}$, $M_S = 0$ and is a combination of $M_L = \bar{1}$.

1	0	$\bar{1}$
	↓	↑

and

1	0	$\bar{1}$
	↑	↓

The wavefunctions χ_i are found to be those given in Table 3.3 in terms of the ϕ_i given previously in Table 3.2. The order in which the χ_i have been written is apparently random, but this particular order simplifies the appearance of the final secular determinant and shows more clearly what is happening.

TABLE 3.3.

χ_i	2-Electron d_ε Wavefunctions	$M_{L_{\mathrm{eff}}}$	M_S
1	$1/\sqrt{2}\,\lvert\phi_1\phi_5\rvert$	$\bar{1}$	1
2	$1/\sqrt{2}\,\lvert\phi_2\phi_4\rvert$	1	$\bar{1}$
3	$1/\sqrt{2}\,\lvert\phi_1\phi_3\rvert$	1	1
4	$1/\sqrt{2}\,\lvert\phi_2\phi_6\rvert$	$\bar{1}$	$\bar{1}$
5	$1/2\,[\lvert\phi_4\phi_5\rvert+\lvert\phi_3\phi_6\rvert]$	0	0
6	$1/\sqrt{2}\,\phi_3\phi_5$	0	1
7	$1/2\,[\lvert\phi_1\phi_6\rvert+\lvert\phi_2\phi_5\rvert]$	$\bar{1}$	0
8	$1/2\,[\lvert\phi_1\phi_4\rvert+\lvert\phi_2\phi_3\rvert]$	1	0
9	$1/\sqrt{2}\,\lvert\phi_4\phi_6\rvert$	0	$\bar{1}$

where

$$\lvert\phi_1\phi_5\rvert \equiv \begin{vmatrix} \phi_1(1) & \phi_1(2) \\ \phi_5(1) & \phi_5(2) \end{vmatrix} = \phi_1(1)\phi_5(2) - \phi_1(2)\phi_5(1)$$

The (1) and (2) refer to electrons 1 and 2, respectively. The actual calculation of the matrix elements will not be given here in detail, since the methods are exactly as used previously for the d_ε^1 calculation. The perturbation secular determinant is finally as follows:

χ_i	1	2	3	4	5	6	7	8	9	
1	$-\frac{1}{2}-E$									
2		$-\frac{1}{2}-E$								
3			$\frac{1}{2}-E$		$\frac{1}{2}$					
4				$\frac{1}{2}-E$	$\frac{1}{2}$					
5			$\frac{1}{2}$	$\frac{1}{2}$	$0-E$					$=0$
6						$0-E$	$\frac{1}{2}$			
7						$\frac{1}{2}$	$0-E$			
8								$0-E$	$\frac{1}{2}$	
9								$\frac{1}{2}$	$0-E$	

and can be broken up into one cubic, two quadratic, and two linear equations. The roots are

$$E = +\lambda \text{ (nondegenerate)}$$

$$= +\lambda/2 \text{ (threefold degenerate)}$$

$$= -\lambda/2 \text{ (fivefold degenerate)}$$

Just as for d_ε^1, it is possible to find the wavefunctions which yield the above eigenvalues and to use them to calculate the splitting caused by an applied magnetic field and so to obtain the susceptibility and μ_{eff} (or n_{eff}). The diagram as finally obtained is given in Fig. 3.3. The second-order terms can be quickly obtained, since all the $H_{ij} = 0$ within any of the three sets. The final values of $H_{ij}^2/\Delta E$ are given in Fig. 3.3.

The expression for n_{eff} is, once again (9, 10, 13), somewhat complicated in form

$$n_{\text{eff}}^2 = \frac{3[5/2x + 15 + (x/2 + 9)e^{-x} - 24e^{-3/2x}]}{x(5 + 3e^{-x} + e^{-3/2x})}$$

and the form of this as a function of kT/λ is plotted in Fig. 3.2. In this case, the asymptotic value as $kT/\lambda \to \infty$ is the same as for two p electrons in the ground term of a free ion (ignoring spin-orbit coupling), i.e., $\sqrt{4S(S+1) + L(L+1)} = \sqrt{8+2} = \sqrt{10}$. This value is approached *from below* similarly to the d_ε^1. The value as $T \to 0$ does not, however, have the value of two free spins without orbital contribution and approaches the value $\sqrt{3/2} \equiv 1.225$. However, fortuitously, for the first-row elements the value is $\sim\sqrt{8} = 2.83$ for room temperature (i.e., $kT/\lambda \sim 1$), which is the value for two free spins. This is an example of one of the reasons why magnetic data at a single temperature are likely, at

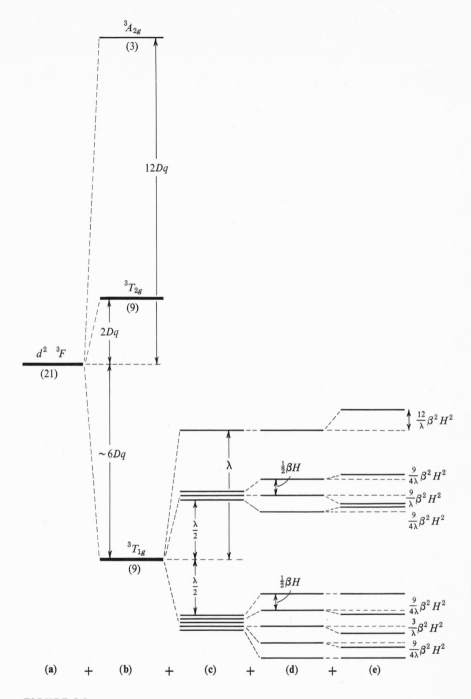

FIGURE 3.3.
(a) field-free ion term + spherically symmetrical terms in the CF potential
(b) octahedral CF
(c) spin-orbit coupling
(d) magnetic field
(e) second-order Zeeman effect

the least, to be misleading with regard to the site symmetry of the paramagnetic ion under investigation. The expression for the d_ε^4 configuration is also obtained by putting $-x$ for x in the d_ε^2 equation with the result that

$$n_{eff}^2 = \frac{3[24 + (x/2 - 9)e^{-x/2} + (5/2\,x - 15)e^{-3/2x}]}{x(1 + 3e^{-x/2} + 5e^{-3/2x})}$$

and the form of this as a function of kT/λ is given in Fig. 3.2. The explanation of the form of the curve should be clear by analogy with the previous discussion.

For complete details and discussion, other references (*3, 4, 10, 11, 13*) should be consulted, particularly ref. (*4*), wherein particular molecules are discussed in detail.

(iv) d_ε^3 Configuration

Since the d_ε^3 configuration yields only a single ^4A term, there is no orbital contribution and the configuration is magnetically simple and of spin-only type.

(v) d_γ^2 Configuration

Only one high-spin term arises from this configuration—$^3A_{2g}$, in an octahedral field and $^3A_2$ in a tetrahedral field. The wavefunctions χ_i are

$$\chi_1 = \frac{1}{\sqrt{2}}|\phi_1\phi_3|$$

$$\chi_2 = \frac{1}{\sqrt{2}}|\phi_2\phi_4|$$

$$\chi_3 = \frac{1}{2}[|\phi_1\phi_4| + |\phi_2\phi_3|]$$

having M_s values of 1, 0 and $\bar{1}$, respectively. There is no spin-orbit splitting, as can be quickly verified and the eigenvalues of $(L_z + 2S_z)$ are simply 2, 0 and $\bar{2}$ respectively.

The susceptibility is, therefore, exactly the same as for two free parallel electron spins.

C. THE g FACTOR IN A CRYSTALLINE FIELD

Now, clearly, the Landé g factor as defined in the introductory discussion pertains only to a field-free ion, since, in a crystalline field, J and /or L cease to be " good " quantum numbers. The definition of g can be modified to allow for its new environment, since it is fundamentally defined by (*23, 13*)

$$g_i = \frac{\Delta E}{\beta H_i} \qquad \text{where } i = x, y, z$$

According to the preceding sections, it is possible to calculate ΔE since

$$\frac{\Delta E}{\beta H_z} = \langle \psi_i | L_z + 2S_z | \psi_i \rangle$$

where the ψ_i are the known linear combinations of the primitive ϕ_i, but are wavefunctions which have been derived on the basis of the Van Vleck–Kotani approximations, i.e., no inclusion of any contributions or interactions from higher *orbital* terms. Whereas this is a reasonable assumption *a priori*, since the magnitude of the crystalline field effects is much larger than those due to spin-orbit coupling, nonetheless, if one is to be more accurate, such terms must be considered. Basically, such consideration is necessary because under the influence of spin-orbit coupling the symmetry properties of two (originally) different terms may become the same, i.e., the terms are said to "become mixed by spin-orbit coupling."

To this end, the "correct" ground-state wavefunctions must be calculated (using perturbation theory, just as previously) including the mixing of the higher crystal field terms. Only then can the correct "g" value for the ion in its particular environment be calculated from the above formula.

To be more specific, the best wavefunctions for the ground state level of a single d electron in an octahedral field, and including spin-orbit coupling, will be a linear combination of the original $^2T_{2g}$ and ^2E_g wavefunctions and the extent to which there will be a contribution from the ^2E_g is clearly dependent both upon the magnitude of the spin-orbit coupling constant λ (or ζ) and the distance apart of the $^2T_{2g} - ^2E_g$ pair of levels, i.e., upon both their λ and Dq dependence. The calculation of these wavefunctions is outside the scope of this text, and is dealt with more than adequately by Ballhausen (3). The net result, however, is that two components of the lower-lying fourfold degenerate level "interact" with the two components of the ^2E_g level and split the degeneracy of the former, with the splitting interval

$$\Delta E = \frac{4\lambda}{10Dq} \beta H_z$$

i.e.,

$$g_z = \frac{4\lambda}{10Dq} \quad (g_z \equiv g_y \equiv g_x \text{ for cubic symmetry})$$

for the case considered. In the absence of mixing the "E_g" levels into the previously fourfold degenerate set ψ_i ($i = 3, 4, 5, 6$—see page 64), the g_z value of the set is zero, so that it is only the "mixed in" excited state which gives g_z a nonzero value. This is usually rather small, being $\sim$2–5 per cent for the first few elements of the first transition series.

The magnitude is not so small, however, in later elements, particularly in such cases as Co^{2+} and Ni^{2+}, where g_z for the lowest term is non-zero. Thus, to the first order in λ, it is possible to write (3, 7, 10, 13, 15)

$$g = g_0 + \frac{2\alpha\lambda}{10Dq}$$

where g_0 applies to the value of g in the absence of spin-orbit coupling and α takes various values (3, 7, 10), according to the particular configuration [and even for small deviations from perfect octahedral symmetry (16)]. Thus, for Ni^{2+}, $\alpha = -4$, $g_0 = 2$, so that

$$g = 2 - \frac{8\lambda}{10Dq}$$

Since g can be measured directly from esr, and Dq can be found from optical spectroscopy, then λ for the complex can be derived. The same type of information can be obtained from magnetic susceptibility measurements, since (10, 15, 16),

$$\mu = \mu_0\left(1 + \frac{\alpha\lambda}{10Dq}\right)$$

where μ_0 is the magnetic moment expected, not including spin-orbit coupling. For $[Ni(H_2O)_6]^{2+}$, $g = 2.25$ from esr (17) and since $g_0 = 2$ and $Dq = 8600\ cm^{-1}$, then $\lambda = -270\ cm^{-1}$. The value of λ for the field-free (uncomplexed) ion (18) is known to be about $-315\ cm^{-1}$, so that there is either a considerable reduction in λ or else the theory is at fault. In fact, both of these factors contribute to the low result for λ. The first matter has already been discussed above (in Chapter 1, page 34) and may be thought of as being due to a combination of electron delocalization and a reduction of the central field charge in which the "magnetic electrons" move. The second factor has not been completely resolved, as yet, but its nature is clear. The value of $-315\ cm^{-1}$ for the free ion comes from the splitting found for the ^3F term of the ion (corrected for some j–j coupling effects) and is therefore a "diagonal" quantity, whereas the λ value obtained from the esr data is an "off-diagonal" quantity and so cannot strictly be directly compared with the former. The extent of error due to this invalid equation is not yet known.

In addition, only the terms in λ have been included; the terms in λ^2 should be added before the result can be compared directly—insofar as it is possible at all—with experiment.

For further calculations of the value of α for the various configurations of interest, more detailed literature should be consulted (3, 7, 10, 13, 15, 16).

D. ADDITIONAL EFFECTS

The final contribution to the susceptibility is the so-called "high-frequency" part. Suppose that an ion or molecule has a ground term ^1A, i.e., no orbital or spin angular momentum. In general, there will be an excited state of the type

^{r}Y, where Y is understood to be either a zero or nonzero orbital angular momentum level and the same applies to the spin multiplicity factor r. If *either* of these is nonzero, a magnetic field *may* mix one or more of the components of the split excited state into the ground state. The ground state behaves, therefore, as though it has a small temperature independent paramagnetic component— even though, in the absence of the magnetic field, it is rigorously a ^{1}A term. Such contributions are found (*3, 4*) in the $MnO_4{}^{-}$ ion, as well as for such species as $[Co(NH_3)_6]^{3+}$ and other "diagmagnetic" complex ions.

Many other even finer interactions occur, such as super-hyperfine coupling and direct and super exchange interaction (*19*), but these are outside the scope of this discussion and are best left to the original literature.

E. SUMMARY

No detailed discussion of the experimental values found for complexes will be given here, since it is intended only that the main features of the topic be discussed. It is clear, however, that the magnetic moment to be expected from a complex will depend markedly upon the symmetry of the environment of the central ion, its spin-orbit coupling, the magnitude of the "crystal field" perturbing the ion, and the temperature at which the measurement is carried out. Representative examples of the various complexes have been discussed fully elsewhere (*4*). For deviations from cubic symmetry other eferences (*3, 16, 20, 21*) should be consulted.

REFERENCES

1. H. Eyring, J. Walter, and G. E. Kimball, *Quantum Chemistry*, Wiley, New York, 1944.
2. J. H. Van Vleck, *Electric and Magnetic Susceptibilities*, Oxford University Press, New York, 1932.
3. C. J. Ballhausen, *Introduction to Ligand Field Theory*, McGraw-Hill, New York, 1962.
4. B. N. Figgis and J. Lewis, "The Magnetochemistry of Complex Compounds," in J. Lewis and R. Wilkins (eds.), *Modern Coordination Chemistry*, Interscience, New York, 1960, chap. VI.
5. R. S. Nyholm, *Quart. Rev. Chem. Soc.* (London) **7**: 377 (1953).
6. R. S. Nyholm, "Complex Compounds of the Transition Metals," Report to the 10th Solvay Council, Brussels, 1956.
7. W. G. Penney and R. Schlapp, *Phys. Rev.* **41**: 194 (1932).
8. J. H. Van Vleck, *J. Chem. Phys.* **3**: 807 (1935).
9. M. Kotani, *J. Phys. Soc.* (Japan) **4**: 293 (1949).
10. B. N. Figgis, *Nature* **182**: 1568 (1958).
11. J. S. Griffith, *Trans. Faraday Soc.* **54**: 1109 (1958).

12. E. U. Condon and G. H. Shortley, *The Theory of Atomic Spectra*, 2d ed., Cambridge Univ. Press, Cambridge, 1953.
13. J. S. Griffith, *The Theory of Transition Metal Ions*, Cambridge Univ. Press, Cambridge, 1961.
14. J. C. Slater, *The Quantum Theory of Atomic Structure*, McGraw-Hill, New York, 1961, vols. I and II.
15. B. N. Figgis, J. Lewis, R. S. Nyholm, and R. D. Peacock, *Discussions Faraday Soc.* [26]: 103 (1958).
16. B. N. Figgis, *Trans. Faraday Soc.* 56: 1553 (1960).
17. J. H. Griffith and J. Owen, *Proc. Roy. Soc.* A213: 459 (1952).
18. T. M. Dunn, *Trans. Faraday Soc.* 57: 1441 (1961).
19. S. Koide and T. Oguchi, *Advan. Chem. Phys.* 5: 189 (1963).
20. B. N. Figgis, *Trans. Faraday Soc.*, 57: 198 (1961).
21. B. N. Figgis, *Trans. Faraday Soc.* 58: 204 (1961).

CHAPTER 4 THE EFFECTS OF INNER-ORBITALS ON THERMODYNAMIC PROPERTIES

DONALD S. McCLURE

The lattice energies of the first transition series dihalides are shown in Fig. 4.1 as a graph of $-U$ vs. atomic number. The form of this curve has been regarded by many people as being peculiar, since it is not monotonic. Ca, Mn, and Zn lie on a nearly straight line, and the two groups of elements in between lie on curves above this line. The simple expectation was that with each added nuclear charge, the ionic radius would be reduced by an approximately similar amount, and there would be a corresponding increase in the Madelung energy of the crystal lattice. This would lead to a monotonic increase of $-U$ with Z.

An explanation was proposed by W. G. Penney (*1*) and then rediscovered by Orgel (*2*) at a time when more attention was given to transition metal ions. A survey article including a critical review of available data has been published by George and McClure (*3*).

In brief, the peculiar nature of the curve can be explained as an effect of the crystal field on the energy of the inner d electrons of the metal ions. The crystal field provides extra stability for these electrons in cases where electronic degeneracy occurs in the ground state of the free ion, but not otherwise. The ions Ca^{++}, Mn^{++}, and Zn^{++} have no degeneracy, whereas the two groups between do.

If we do not assume an ionic model for the compound, the explanation may take different forms, as will be discussed later. However, the removal of the electronic degeneracy by the crystal must always occur, and will make some contribution to the heat of formation. The unique aspects of the thermodynamic

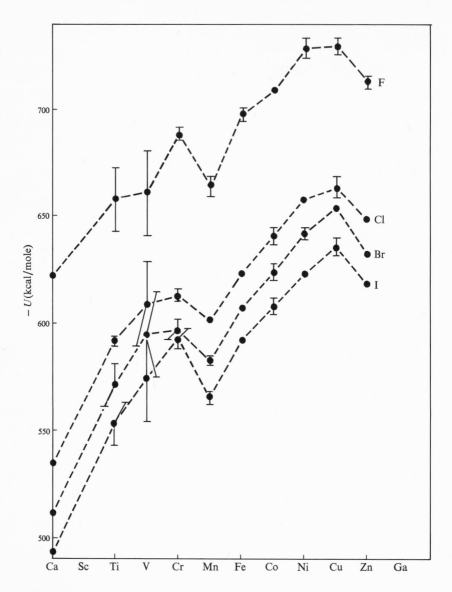

FIGURE 4.1.
The lattice energies of the transition metal dihalides.

properties of transition metal ions arise from the occurrence of the electronic degeneracy and its partial removal by the crystal field.

By way of contrast, compounds like NaCl or $CaCl_2$ are well represented as consisting of anions and cations in $^1S_0$ states. The lowest atomic levels above the ground $^1S_0$ level lie many volts higher and have no influence on the thermo-dynamic properties of the compound.

In another extreme example, a valence crystal such as diamond may be thought to be formed from carbon atoms in highly degenerate states, and to this extent is analogous to transition metal compounds. But the degeneracy is so strongly removed by bond formation that the excited states are well beyond the range of chemical interest. The heat of formation of diamond cannot be divided con-veniently into an electronic part and a coulomb part as in the transition metal compounds.

A further contrast is provided by the rare earth salts. Very slight irregularities in the curve of $-U$ vs. Z are observed, reminiscent of those in the transition series. But the inner $4f$ shell splits by such a small amount that the electronic stabilization may be neglected for most purposes, and the slope of the $-U$ vs. Z curve is mainly determined by the lanthanide contraction.

Even between the three transition series there are quite important differences in the extent of the crystal field splitting and, therefore, in the resultant effect on on the lattice energies.

The actual magnitude of the electronic stabilization for cubic fields computed on the ionic model is shown in Fig. 4.2. We can imagine the crystal forming from free ions arranged in the symmetry of the crystal lattice but all at great distances apart at first. Then the energies of the electrons in the fivefold de-generate D state, for example, will all be equal. As the interionic distances decrease the fivefold degeneracy can no longer be supported because the highest degeneracy possible in a solid is 3 (cubic crystals). If the process of formation is isothermal, electrons will have to lie predominantly in the lower of the energy levels created by the splitting of the D level, subject to the restrictions of the Pauli Principle. Thus energy must be removed from the system, and it will appear as an increment in U.

For the very important case of the cubic field there is only one splitting parameter, often called Dq. Figure 4.2 applies to the cubic case, and to the three varieties of cubic coordination—octahedral, tetrahedral, and cubal.

The diagram in Fig. 4.2(a) can be thought of either as an orbital diagram which applies to each electron of the ion or as the splitting diagram of a multi-electron D state. In the former case it can be applied to obtain the stabilization energy for any number of d electrons in a cubic field. A d orbital thus splits into two sets belonging, respectively, to the T_2 and E representations of the cubic group. The T_2 orbital lies lower than E in an octahedral field; the inverse is true for a tetrahedral or cubal field. The reason for this is that the e orbitals point toward the anions in an octahedral field and, because the negative anions repel electrons, the energy of the e electrons is raised. The t orbitals point away from the anions, and their energy is not raised by as much. The zero of energy in the ionic model is chosen as the average of the t and e orbital energies, so that the splitting stabilizes the t and destabilizes the e orbitals relative to this reference

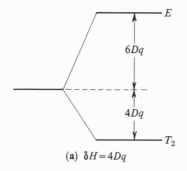

upright for:

d^1, d^6 (Ti^{+++}, Fe^{++}, Co^{+++})

inverted for:

d^4, d^9 (Cr^{++}, Mn^{+++}, Cu^{++})

(a) $\delta H = 4Dq$

d^2, d^7(V^{+++}, Co^{++})

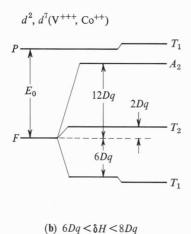

(b) $6Dq < \delta H < 8Dq$

d^3, d^8(V^{++}, Cr^{+++}, Ni^{++})

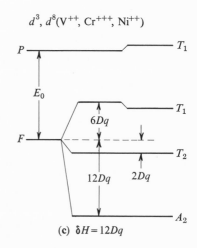

(c) $\delta H = 12Dq$

FIGURE 4.2.

(a) splitting diagrams for d orbitals, or for D states

(b), (c) splitting diagrams for P and F states

The diagrams are appropriate for octahedral fields as they stand, and when inverted apply to tetrahedral or cubal coordination. The value of δH is the energy of the lowest state below the unperturbed level. The diagrams also give the positions of spectral bands, and can be used to derive Dq from spectroscopic data.

level. In the other cubic figures, the t orbitals point more directly toward the anions than do the e orbitals, so the relative stabilities are reversed.

The relative orbital displacements are inversely proportional to their degeneracies so the t orbital is stabilized by $4Dq$, and the e orbital is destabilized by $6Dq$. The net effect for several electrons is

$$\delta H = xDq = (4N_t - 6N_e)Dq \qquad (1)$$

where N_t and N_e are the numbers of electrons in the two kinds of orbital. This is not yet a prescription for calculating the energy of stabilization, as we do not know, *a priori* for a given atom, what its electron distribution will be.

The electron distribution depends on the relative magnitudes of the crystal field splitting and the pairing energy. The latter is the energy required to place two electrons in the same orbital. It enters the problem in the following way: As we add electrons to the ion, the first three will be able to go into the three t orbitals with parallel spins, thus following Hund's rule for atoms and minimizing their mutual electrostatic repulsion. The fourth will either have to pair up with an electron in one of the t orbitals, thus incurring a large electron repulsion, or be raised to an e orbital. In either case there will be a destabilization of the electrons. This dual possibility of promotion or pairing occurs for four, five, six, or seven electrons in an octahedral field. Equation (1) is not complete, since the pairing energy is not shown. It must therefore be modified to

$$\delta H = (4N_t - 6N_e)Dq + P \tag{2}$$

The electron distribution in the four-electron case will be $3t + 1e$ when $10Dq < P$, and $4t$ when $10Dq > P$, i.e., the distribution observed in the ground state must correspond to the one having the lowest energy.

The distinction between states having maximum possible spin multiplicity and those with a lower multiplicity is an important one. The spin state of the ion affects not only the thermodynamic properties of its compounds, but the magnetic and chemical ones as well.

The calculation of the pairing energies is given in ref. (4) for transition metal ions, and in ref. (5) for rare earth and actinide ions.

Experimental values of Dq for various ions and coordination types are given in Table 4.1. When an experimental value for some situation of interest is lacking, Dq may be estimated by a variety of methods. Using a point ion model of an octahedral complex it can be shown that

$$Dq = \frac{35}{4} \cdot \frac{Ze}{R^5} \overline{r^4} \tag{3}$$

where R is the metal-anion distance, $\overline{r^4}$ is the mean value of the electron radius to the fourth power, and Ze is the charge of the anion. A similar calculation for tetrahedral and cubal geometries gives different values of the numerical coefficient so that, for the same R,

$$Dq(\text{oct}) = -\frac{9}{4} Dq(\text{tetr}) = -\frac{9}{8} Dq(\text{cub}) \tag{4}$$

The first relationship is experimentally quite well tested and verified. There are as yet no cases of cubal geometry suitable for testing the second. The distance dependence given in Eq. (3) is approximately correct in one sense. Both thermal

TABLE 4.1. CRYSTAL FIELD THEORY DATA FOR TRANSITION METAL IONS

Number of d-electrons	Ion	Free ion ground state	Octa-hedral field ground state	Tetra-hedral field ground state	Dq cm^{-1} oct.	Dq cm^{-1} tetr.	Stabilization, kcal oct.	Stabilization, kcal tetr.	Oct. site preference energy kcal/mole
1	Ti^{+++}	^2D	$^2T_{2g}$	^2E_g	2030	900	23.1	15.4	7.7
2	V^{+++}	^3F	$^3T_{1g}$	$^3A_{2g}$	1800	840	41.5	28.7	12.8
3	V^{++}	^4F	$^4A_{2g}$	$^4T_{1g}$	1180	520	40.2	8.7	31.5
3	Cr^{+++}	^4F	$^4A_{2g}$	$^4T_{1g}$	1760	780	60.0	13.3	46.7
4	Cr^{++}	^5D	^5E_g	$^5T_{2g}$	1400	620	24.0	7.0	17.0
4	Mn^{+++}	^5D	^5E_g	$^5T_{2g}$	2100	930	35.9	10.6	25.3
5	Mn^{++}	^6S	$^6A_{1g}$	$^6A_{1g}$	750	330	0	0	0
5	Fe^{+++}	^6S	$^6A_{1g}$	$^6A_{1g}$	1400	620	0	0	0
6	Fe^{++}	^5D	$^5T_{2g}$	^5E_g	1000	440	11.4	7.5	3.9
6	(a)Co^{+++}	^5D	$^1A_{1g}$	^5E_g		780	45	26	19
7	Co^{++}	^4F	$^4T_{1g}$	$^4A_{2g}$	1000	440	17.1	15.0	2.1
8	Ni^{++}	^3F	$^3A_{2g}$	$^3T_{1g}$	860	380	29.3	6.5	22.8
9	Cu^{++}	^2D	^2E_g	$^2T_{2g}$	1300	580	22.2	6.6	15.6
10	Zn^{++}	^1S	$^1A_{1g}$	$^1A_{1g}$	0	0	0	0	0

The data given are:
1. Number of d electrons.
2. Transition metal ions.
3. Free ion Russell–Saunders ground term (spin-orbit coupling is neglected in the term designation).
4. The standard group theory symbol for the ground state of the octahedrally coordinated ion in a solid (using nomenclature of Eyring, Walter, and Kimball, *Quantum Chemistry*).
5. The group theory symbol for the tetrahedrally coordinated ionic ground state.
6. Dq values for octahedral hydrates of the ions.
7. Dq calculated for tetrahedral coordination. *See* ref. (3).
8, 9. The thermodynamic stabilization in octahedral or tetrahedral fields.
10. The octahedral site preference, or the difference between columns 8 and 9.

(a) The octahedral site stabilization of Co^{+++} was estimated from the heat of hydration increment caused by the crystal field, and the tetrahedral site stabilization was taken to be the same as for Cr^{+++}.

expansion (*6*) and pressure (*7*) experiments given an exponent of 5 or 6. This does not mean, however, that Dq can be calculated for an ion in different lattices by simply inserting a new radius in Eq. (3). The actual situation is much more complicated.

Also shown in Fig. 4.2 is the way the splitting varies with the type of ground state. There are only three types of ground terms having maximum spin multiplicity—*S*, *D*, and *F*—and only the latter two are split by the crystal field. The splitting may be upright or inverted, as shown in Fig. 4.2. Other types of ground term may occur as a result of spin pairing in the crystal field, and in the ionic

model these are considered to arise from combinations of excited levels of the
d shell. These are best treated by the orbital method already described.

The heat of formation of ionic compounds is often analyzed in terms of the
Born–Haber cycle. In brief, there are three steps. The first two are the prepara-
tion of the positive and negative ions from the elements in their standard states.
The "prepared states" are ordinarily the lowest $^1S_0$ states of the ions. The third
step is the condensation of the gas into a crystal, with release of the lattice energy.
For a transition metal ion, the "prepared state" must be similar to the state of
the ion in the crystal: in particular, it must have the same number of d electrons.
Furthermore, since we are considering an entire transition series in which the
ion in the crystal contains one more d electron for each increment in Z, we must
select a series of similar states for the free ions as standard reference states.
Fortunately we know the ionization energies to the lowest state of the d^n configuration of each $+2$ and $+3$ ion of the first transition series, and this is the
standard prepared state to use in the Born–Haber cycle.

There is a fourth step in the Born–Haber cycle in case we are dealing with
transition ions; it is, of course, the crystal field splitting. The heat of formation
is therefore written

$$\Delta H_f = H_p{}^+ + H_p{}^- + U^0 + \delta H \tag{5}$$

The ordinary lattice energy U^0 is written as

$$-U = H_p{}^+ + H_p{}^- - \Delta H_f \tag{6}$$

and this is what has been plotted in the figures. We now see that

$$U = U^0 + \delta H \tag{7}$$

where U^0 is the lattice energy for a hypothetical crystal in which the d electrons
ignore the crystal field and retain their gas-phase degeneracy. The variation of
U with atomic number comes from the term δH, as U^0 is expected to vary mono-
tonically. Since Dq also varies only slowly, the crystal field stabilization factor
x is responsible for the main effects. Its value can be obtained from Eq. (1), and
corrections for spin pairing may also be made if necessary.

Since x is a purely theoretical factor, an independent test of the theory would
be to see if values of Dq obtained from spectroscopic data, multiplied by the
appropriate x, would correct the U values to U^0, supposedly a smoothly varying
function of Z. This can be done for the heats of hydration, as shown in Fig. 4.3.
(Low-spin ground states do not occur in the hydrates.) The values of Dq for the
hydrated ions were used, and the "corrected" heats of hydration are plotted
against Z. These values do indeed lie on a nearly smooth curve. This result
constitutes the best confirmation of the present explanation for the shape of
the U vs. Z curves.

At this point we can make some applications of the idea of crystal field stabilization, although we are not through with a critical examination of it.

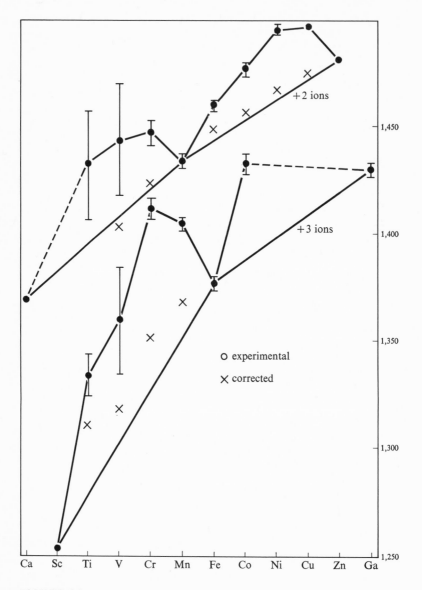

FIGURE 4.3.
Heats of hydration of transition metal ions. Values of δH derived from spectroscopic values of Dq are subtracted from each hydration energy and these points are indicated by an X. The straight-line interpolation curves are also shown.

One interesting application is to calculate the site preference, or coordination preference energies. When an ion has two coordination possibilities, the crystal field energy for the two may be different, and may in fact be the deciding factor as to which coordination is adopted.

The site-preference idea was proposed independently by several authors in 1957 (8, 9) and several examples of its usefulness and correctness were presented at that time. It is an idea that can easily be stretched too far, and this was promptly done. It must be remembered that crystal field effects are small and can be masked by other things. The only way they can be uncovered is by a thorough comparison of several members of a transition series, including elements which should not have a crystal field stabilization.

The best such example is the equilibrium between normal and inverse spinels. The spinels are double oxides having the general formula $A[B_2]O_4$. The oxygens lie in a close packed cubic lattice; the A^{++} ions occupy one eighth of the tetrahedral holes in the oxygen lattice, and the B^{+++} ions occupy one half of the octahedral holes. There is a so-called inverse structure $B[AB]O_4$, wherein the A and half of the B ions have changed places. The problem is to explain the relative stability of the normal and inverse structures.

If we assume that the only important factor determining which structure is the more stable is crystal field energy, it is a simple matter to make a set of predictions. Fortunately there are plenty of data with which to make comparisons. The last column of Table 4.1 shows the value of δH (octahedral) $- \delta H$ (tetrahedral), called the octahedral site-preference energy. This quantity varies from zero for Mn^{++}, Fe^{+++}, etc., to 22.8 kcal for Ni^{++} and 46.7 for Cr^{+++}, for example; so it amounts to several per cent of the lattice energy. Table 4.2 shows some predicted cation distributions compared to experimental facts. All spinels containing Cr^{+++} are predicted and found to be normal. Most spinels containing Ni^{++} are predicted and found to be inverse.

The extent of the agreement is rather surprisingly good, particularly when it is remembered that both the Madelung and repulsion energies, which are many times larger than crystal field energies, change when the cations interchange. Verwey and Heilmann (10) studied the dependence of the Madelung energy on the crystal parameters and found that a normal and inverse structure could have the same energy within commonly observed ranges of the parameters. Therefore the possibility that the crystal field energy is the determining factor can at least be made to seem reasonable. Miller (11) has recently done the site-preference calculation using Madelung, repulsion, and crystal field terms, and has been able to remove most of the discrepancies which the simple theory could not explain. Thus one cannot assume that the crystal field energy is the sole determiner of the cation distribution, but it would be quite wrong to ignore it.

The same conclusion can be stated for other cases of coordination equilibrium. Gruen (12) has found some cases in solutions of transition metal compounds in molten alkali halides which appear to follow the crystal field predictions without requiring any other considerations. Katzin (*13*), on the other hand, appears to have found some cases which go counter to the predictions of crystal field theory. Unfortunately his immediate conclusion was that crystal field theory is of no particular importance, whereas one should look for the other factors which must always be considered simultaneously with it.

TABLE 4.2. THEORETICAL AND EXPERIMENTAL CATION DISTRIBUTIONS IN 2–3 SPINELS, $A[B_2]O_4$

$\diagdown$ B A $\diagdown$	Al^{+++}		Ga^{+++}		Fe^{+++}		Cr^{+++}		Mn^{+++}		V^{+++}		Co^{+++}	
	Exp.	Th.	Exp.	Th.	Exp.	Th.	Exp.	Th.	Exp.	Th.	Exp.	Th.	Exp.	Th.
Mg^{++}	$.88I^{(e)}$	0	$I^{(c)}$	0	$I^{(a)}$	0	$N^{(a)}$	N		N	$N^{(d)(f)}$	N		N
Zn^{++}	$N^{(a)}$	0	N	0	$N^{(a)}$	0	$N^{(a)}$	N	$N, T^{(b,g)}$	N	$N^{(d)(f)}$	N		N
Cd^{++}	$N^{(a)}$	0	$N^{(d)}$	0	$N^{(a)}$	0	$N^{(a)}$	N		N		N		N
Mn^{++}	$N^{(a)}$	0		0	$I^{(a)}$	0	$N^{(a)}$	N		N	$N^{(f)}$	N		N
Fe^{++}	$N^{(a)}$	I		I	$I^{(a)}$	I	$N^{(a)}$	N		N	$N^{(f)}$	$I+N$		N
Co^{++}	$N^{(a)}$	I		I	$I^{(a)}$	I	$N^{(a)}$	N		N		$I+N$		N
Ni^{++}	$\frac{3}{4}I+\frac{1}{4}N^{(b)}$	I	$I^{(h)}$	I	$I^{(a)}$	I	$N^{(a)}$	N		$I+N$		I		I
Cu^{++}	$I^{(a)}$	I		I	$0.86I, T^{(e)}$	I	$N^{(a)}$	N		N		I		N

N = normal I = inverse T = tetragonal   0 = no prediction is made by d shell theory

[a] Verwey E. J. W. and Heilman E. L. *J. Chem. Phys.* **15**: 174 (1947).
[b] Romeijn F. C. *Philips Res. Rep.* **8**: 304 321 (1953).
[c] Barth T. F. W. and Posnjak E. *Z. Kristallogr.* **82**: 325 (1932).
[d] Rudorff W. and Reuter B. *Z. Anorg. Chem.* **253**: 194 (1947).
[e] Bertaut E. *J. Phys. Radium* **12**: 252 (1951)
[f] Lovell G. H. B. *Transit. Brit. Ceram. Soc.* **50**: 315 (1951).
[g] Mason B. *Amer. Min.* **32**: 426 (1947).
[h] Greenwald S., Pickart S. and Grannis F. *J. Chem. Phys.* **22**: 1597 (1954).

Robbins (*14*) has shown that divalent ions which have an octahedral site preference in spinels have a tetrahedral site preference when F^- ion is substituted for some of the $O^=$. Such a substitution requires a valence change of some of the trivalent ions. There is thus a rather radical change in the coulomb fields at octahedral and tetrahedral sites, and the crystal field predictions alone are not expected to apply. However, the crystal field effects did show some force; for example, in the magnetoplumbite structure $BaGa_{12}O_{19}$, Ni^{++} was less stabilized in the tetrahedral site by F^- substitution than Co^{++}; and this is the relative behavior predicted by crystal field theory.

Another application of the stabilization energies is to analysis of the oxidation-reduction potentials. The ligand field effect changes sharply with the number of electrons, and if this is recognized, the change of oxidation potential through a series of transition metal ions makes much more sense. It should in fact follow closely the ionization potential of the ion. For the reactions:

$$M_{(aq)}^{++} + H_{(aq)}^{+} \rightarrow M_{(aq)}^{+++} + \tfrac{1}{2}H_{2,(g)} \tag{8}$$

the free energy can be written:

$$\Delta F^0 = \Delta H_H(3+) - \Delta H_H(2+) + I_3$$
$$- T[S(3+) - S(2+)] - T\Delta S(H^+ \to \tfrac{1}{2}H_2) \tag{9}$$

where ΔH_H is a heat of hydration, I_3 the third ionization potential and the others are entropy terms. If the latter stay constant, then the chief variations of ΔF^0 with atomic number come from I_3 and the crystal field terms contained in ΔH_H. The values of $\delta H(3+) - \delta H(2+)$, the crystal field stabilization energy change can be found from Table 4.1. These values are subtracted from the observed ΔF^0 to give the points shown in Fig. 4.4. These "corrected" values fall very close to the values of I_3, also shown in Fig. 4.4. The agreement is so good, for at least the elements V through Co, that other terms must not produce large variations with atomic number.

The curve of heat of sublimation of the transition metals vs. atomic number has the same appearance as the curve of heat of formation of ionic crystals (see Fig. 4.5). This suggests that there is an explanation for the sublimation energies involving the crystal field energy. However, Griffith (15) showed that this is not so, and it will be interesting to examine his results in order to deepen our understanding of the crystal field stabilization energy and to foster some caution about using it everywhere.

The heat of sublimation of a metal can be written as

$$-\Delta H = xDq + b + P \tag{10}$$

where xDq is the crystal field stabilization energy, b is the bond energy, and P is the valence state promotion energy. Since the heat of sublimation of metals is nearly independent of the crystalline modification, it follows that xDq, the crystal field stabilization energy is small, and unimportant.

The bond energy b increases at the beginning of a period with the number of electrons available for bonding. Griffith assumed that the $3d$ and $4s$ orbitals were available in the transition region, giving a total of six orbitals. The bonding contribution therefore increases until six electrons have been added (Cr) and decreases to zero at Zn when each metal atom has twelve electrons. After zinc, the p orbitals are used for bonding. This exclusion of the p orbitals until after zinc is an oversimplification, but it is not a bad approximation.

The final quantity in ΔH is the promotion energy P, and it is this which causes the dip in the middle of the transition series. As the number of electrons increases, so does the electron repulsion, and the energy required to raise the metal from its ground state to the valence state therefore also increases. This energy is actually that required to destroy spin-coupling within the atom, since in order to form bonds, the spins *between* atoms must be coupled. It is at a maximum in the middle of the series (d^5s) and there reduces the heat of sublimation by a substantial amount.

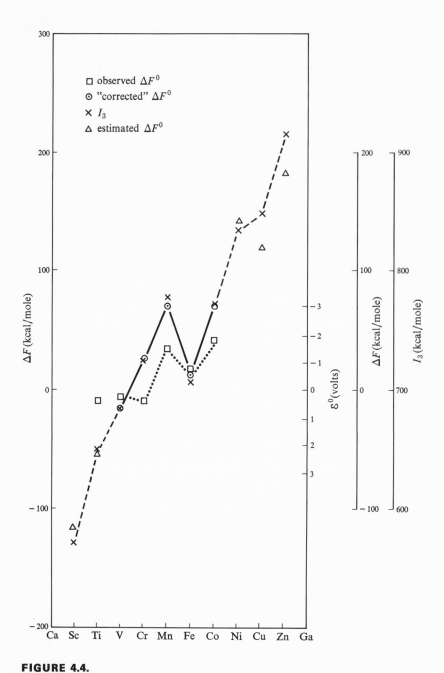

FIGURE 4.4.

The $M^{++} \rightarrow M^{+++}$ oxidation potentials of the first transition series. The "corrected" $\Delta F°$ values are the observed ones minus the crystal field correction, $[\delta H(3+) - \delta H(2+)]$.

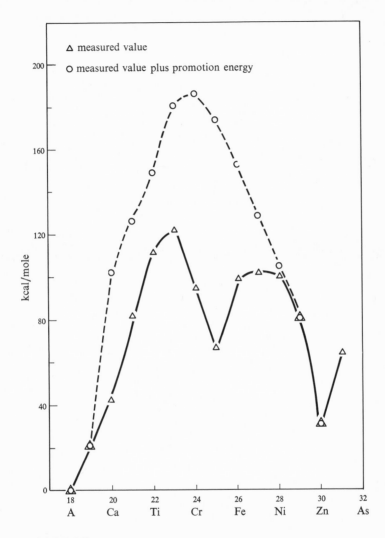

FIGURE 4.5.
Heats of sublimation of transtition metals. The "corrected" values in this case are supposed theoretically to be the bonding energies, and it is seen that they do follow a curve of the type expected.

The calculation of P may be carried out in terms of atomic spectral parameters. We must first raise each atom from its ground state to the lowest state of the bonding configuration $d^{n-1}s$. Then we must add the spin-decoupling energy. The first part is simply a measured atomic term. For example, vanadium has the ground term $^3F(3d^34s^2)$ and must be excited to $^6D(3d^44s)$, 2200 cm^{-1} higher (*16*).

The second part is $1/2 \Sigma K_{ij}$, where K_{ij} is the exchange integral between orbitals containing one electron. The orbitals chosen are the ones giving the Hund Rule ground state of the configuration. The exchange integrals may be found from the analysis of atomic spectra.

According to Eq. (10), $P + \Delta H = -b$, and a plot of $P + \Delta H$ vs. Z should show a maximum in the middle of the period at Cr. The actual results of Griffith are shown in Fig. 4.5, and it is seen that there is such a curve and that it actually has a maximum where the bonding energy is expected to be greatest. (Griffith used incorrect data in his paper; the correct data presented in Fig. 4.5 make his idea seem even better.)

It is reasonable that in the formation of metals, the normally unfilled np shell should not be strongly involved because it is 50 to 70 kcal above the ns and $(n - 1)d$ shell energies for all three transition groups, and the energy of the metal-metal bond is only slightly greater than this. In salts, the d to p promotion energy is compensated for by the larger binding energy. Thus in the metals we can speak of a " shell" capable of containing 12 electrons in ds hybrid orbitals, and in the salts a dsp "shell" of 18.

In a metal the distinction between bonding and antibonding orbitals is not useful, because the two classes are of nearly the same energy and equally occupied. At the other extreme, there are the neutral carbonyl compounds whose formulae, such as $Cr(CO)_6$, $Fe(CO)_5$, $Ni(CO)_4$ are determined by the number of electrons needed to fill the $3d$, $4s$ and $4p$ shells to a total of 18. There are no electrons in antibonding orbitals in their ground states.

In the ionic salts, which form a class intermediate between the metals and the carbonyls, there may be d electrons in antibonding orbitals in the ground states. For the lower valent ionic salts, the d shell of 10 closes the series of possible compounds, while for the trivalent and higher valency compounds, there is a tendency for the t shell of six to terminate the series of (octahedral) compounds, since the t to e promotion energy is large.

These statements apply to compounds having anions without available orbitals in them. When the ligands contain empty low lying π-orbitals, the compounds that can form are those capable of π-bonding, (17) and the electrons which in simple ionic compounds were classed as antibonding, are in these cases π-bonding

The crystal field theory does not work quite as well for $+3$ ions as for $+2$ ions. The subtraction of the spectroscopic values of Dq does not produce quite as good a straight line for the $+3$ ions as for the $+2$, as can be seen for the hydration energies in Fig. 4.3. The d^5 ion in this series, Fe^{+++}, lies well above the line joining Sc^{+++} and Ga^{+++}. The lattice energies of the trivalent halides shown in Fig. 4.6 behave in a way similar to the hydration energies. Perhaps the most significant feature of these curves is the rapid increase of lattice energy in the first half of the series, contrasted to the much smaller change in the second half.

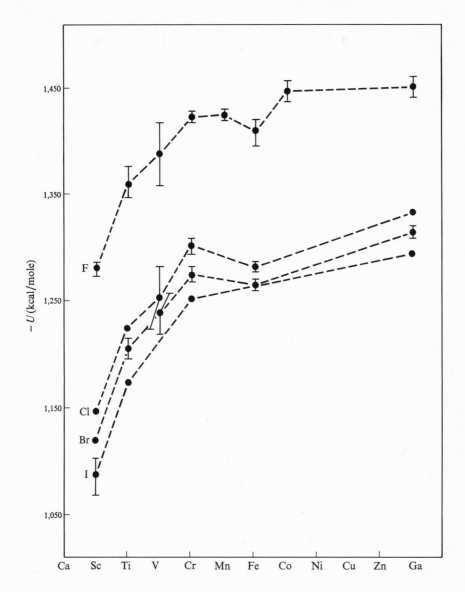

FIGURE 4.6.
Lattice energies of the trivalent halides.

It is undoubtedly true that the trivalent ions make more use of covalent bonding than divalent ions. Since this is so, the effect of promotion energy for hybrid bond formation must be superimposed on the lattice energy curves. The promotion energy is not important in the early part of the series, hence the rapid increase of lattice energy; however, it becomes important later on where it slows down the rate of increase. Since the amount of covalent bonding must change from one ion to the next, it is not easy to make quantitative statements as to what should happen. The qualitative idea seems reasonable, however, and it shows that the crystal field approach cannot be considered as being complete in itself.

We return now to the simple electrostatic crystal field picture to take up a point which was ignored earlier. We said that as the atomic number increases the ionic radius is expected to decrease. This is because for each added nuclear charge, the *d* electron which is also added does not completely shield the nucleus. However, this decrease of radius is not a smooth one, because the different types of *d* orbital, *t* and *e* for the cubic case, do not have the same shielding power. The first three electrons added go into *t* orbitals which in an octahedral field point away from the ligands. Thus a greater decrease in radius is expected than if *e* orbitals pointing toward the ligands were being filled. The actual form of the curve of radius vs. atomic number is given in Fig. 4.7, where it is seen that the ions Ca^{++}, Mn^{++}, Zn^{++} lie on a nearly straight line (in the series of MO compounds having the NaCl structure), and the other ions lie below it at smaller radii. The explanation just given for the form of this curve was first proposed by Van Santen and Van Weiringen (*18*).

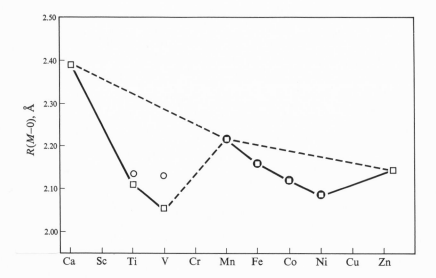

FIGURE 4.7.
Metal-oxygen distance in divalent transition metal oxides (in Å). The dashed lines gives the radii which would supposedly occur without the crystal field effect. The points enclosed by circles are the values of the M-O distance computed from the dashed curve and the crystal field contraction effect.

In our discussion of the thermodynamic stabilization effects we ignored these fluctuations in the curve of radius vs. Z, and we now want to see what effect they have on the explanation of the stabilization by the crystal field. We previously assumed that we could calculate the hypothetical lattice energy, $-U^0$, of a transition metal compound by taking the ion with its d electrons randomized among all the d orbitals; then the correct lattice energy would result from the stabilization of the electrons in their preferred orbitals giving $+U = +U^0 + \delta H$, where δH is the electronic stabilization energy. However, the lattice constant in the hypothetical state having the electrons randomized is larger than in the final state, and in fact probably corresponds to the points interpolated between Ca–Mn–Zn in Fig. 4.7. Let us call this interpolated lattice constant R_0, and write

$$U^0 = F(R_0) \tag{11}$$

where F is a lattice energy function defined for a range of R values. Call the true equilibrium distance R_e and write

$$U = F(R_e) + E_c(R_e) \tag{12}$$

where $E_c(R_e)$ is the electronic stabilization energy in the real crystal. The thermodynamic stabilization is therefore

$$\delta H = U - U^0 = F(R_e) - F(R_0) + E_c(R_e) \tag{13}$$

rather than only $E_c(R_e)$, as was supposed earlier. The quantity $F(R_e) - F(R_0)$ can be looked upon as the energy required to compress the lattice from R_0 to R_e; the energy required comes from the increase in Dq as the lattice contracts. The new term therefore represents a destablization of the lattice. The analysis tells us that the correct value of Dq to use in computing thermodynamic stability is the one for $R = R_0$, rather than for $R = R_e$. If this smaller value of Dq were used, the $F(R_0) - F(R_e)$ term would be omitted. This result does not agree with the experimental facts that the thermodynamic stabilization is always larger than the one calculated from spectroscopic data. Some of these experimental results are illustrated in Fig. 4.3; others are given in ref. (3).

Nevertheless, by an extension of the above analysis Hush and Pryce (19) were able to calculate the lattice contraction fairly accurately. In the equilibrium position of the real crystal we must have from Eq. (12)

$$U'(R_e) = F'(R_e) + E_c'(R_e) = 0 \tag{14}$$

This equation represents the equilibrium between the forces tending to expand $[F'(R_e)]$ and compress $[E_c'(R_e)]$ the lattice. In the hypothetical crystal in which the crystal field contracting force has been turned off, we have

$$U'(R_0) = F'(R_0) = 0 \tag{15}$$

Now we can express F' in terms of a Taylor series expansion about the point R_e

$$F'(R) = F'(R_e) + F''(R_e)\delta R + \dots \tag{16}$$

where $\delta R = R - R_e$. If we terminate the series at the δR term (since δR is small) and compute $F'(R_0)$ from the series, we can write

$$F'(R_0) = F'(R_e) + F''(R_e)\delta R_e = 0 \tag{17}$$

where $\delta R_e = R_0 - R_e$. This equation when solved for δR_e gives the lattice contraction

$$\delta R_e = -\frac{F'(R_e)}{F''(R_e)} = \frac{E_c{'}(R_e)}{F''(R_e)} \tag{18}$$

The equation simply says that the contraction equals the ratio of force to force constant.

At this point we can substitute particular forms for the functions $E_c(R)$ and $F(R)$:

$$E_c(R) = \frac{C}{R^5} = xDq, \qquad F(R) = -\frac{A}{R} + \frac{B}{R^n} \tag{19}$$

and

$$E_c{'}(R_e) = -\frac{5C}{R^6} = -\frac{5xDq}{R}, \qquad F''(R_e) = -\frac{2A}{R_e{}^3} + \frac{n(n+1)B}{r^{n+2}}$$

The value of Dq to use here is the spectroscopic one. The analysis to this point is essentially the same as that of Hush and Pryce. They evaluated $F''(R_e)$ from the compressibility. The quantity x is known and varies strongly from one ion to the next as shown in Table 4.1. Thus, all of the constants are known and a theoretical δR_e value may be calculated. The values calculated by Hush and Pryce are very close to the measured values as shown in Fig. 4.7.

We now see that the analysis which explains the δr values does not account for the approximately 10 per cent of the crystal field correction that would be needed to make the U vs. Z curve into a straight line. In fact, it increases the departure from a straight line by requiring us to use values of Dq for the expanded lattice. In the case of NiO, the total correction falls short by 25 per cent of the value required to reach the straight line.

At this point it is best to look back on the accomplishments of crystal field theory and to realize how well it works in spite of its simplicity. It is also important to recognize that it has its limits, and in trying to explain good data we have been forced to stop with incomplete qualitative explanations. To go further will require detailed studies of bonding several orders of magnitude more complicated than crystal field theory.

REFERENCES

1. W. G. Penney, *Trans. Faraday Soc.* **35**: 627 (1940).
2. L. E. Orgel, *J. Chem. Soc.* **1952**: 4756.

3. P. George and D. S. McClure, "The Effect of Inner Orbital Splitting on the Thermodynamic Properties of Transition Metal Compounds and Coordination Complexes," in F. A. Cotton (ed.), *Progress in Inorganic Chemistry*, vol. I, Interscience, New York, 1959, pp. 381–464.

4. L. E. Orgel, *J. Chem. Phys.* **23**: 1819 (1955); J. S. Griffith, *J. Inorg. and Nucl. Chem.* **2**: 1, 229 (1956).

5. L. E. Orgel and J. S. Griffith, *J. Chem. Phys.* **26**: 988 (1957).

6. D. S. McClure, *J. Chem. Phys.* **36**: 2757 (1962).

7. P. Bloomfield, A. W. Lawson and C. Rey, *J. Chem. Phys.* **34**: 749 (1961).

8. D. S. McClure, *J. Chem. Phys. Solids* **3**: 311 (1957).

9. J. D. Dunitz and L. E. Orgel, *J. Chem. Phys. Solids* **3**: 318 (1957).

10. E. J. W. Verwey and E. L. Heilmann, *J. Chem. Phys.* **15**: 174 (1947).

11. A. Miller, *J. Appl. Phys.* **30**: 245 (1959).

12. E. Iberson, R. Gut and D. M. Gruen, *J. Phys. Chem.* **66**: 65 (1962); D. M. Gruen, *J. Inorg. and Nucl. Chem.* **4**: 74 (1957).

13. L. Katzin, *J. Chem. Phys.* **35**: 467 (1961); **36**: 3034 (1962).

14. M. Robbins, "Fluoride Compensated Cation Substitutions in Oxides," Thesis, Polytechnic Institute of Brooklyn, June 1962.

15. J. S. Griffith, *J. Inorg. and Nucl. Chem.* **3**: 15 (1956).

16. H. A. Skinner and F. H. Sumner, *J. Inorg. and Nucl. Chem.* **4**: 245 (1957); G. Pilcher and H. A. Skinner, *J. Inorg. and Nucl. Chem.* **7**: 8 (1958).

17. J. Chatt, *J. Inorg. and Nucl. Chem.* **8**: 515 (1958).

18. J. H. Van Santen and J. S. Van Weiringen, *Rec. Trav. Chim. Pays Bas* **71**: 420 (1952).

19. N. S. Hush and M. H. L. Pryce, *J. Chem. Phys.* **28**: 244 (1958).

CHAPTER 5 CRYSTAL FIELD THEORY AND SUBSTITUTION REACTIONS OF METAL IONS

RALPH G. PEARSON

Substitution reactions in inorganic chemistry include the replacement of one ligand (Y and X) by another in a coordination complex, or one metal ion (M and M') by another. Following the terminology of Hughes and Ingold developed for organic reactions, these can be called S_N (nucleophilic substitution) and S_E (electrophilic substitution), reactions, respectively.

$$Y + M\text{–}X \rightarrow M\text{–}Y + X \qquad S_N \qquad (1)$$

$$M' + M\text{–}X \rightarrow M'\text{–}X + M \qquad S_E \qquad (2)$$

It is convenient to exclude those substitution reactions which involve changes in oxidation number. With this proviso, substitution reactions become generalized acid-base reactions in which the metal ions, or positively charged central atoms in general, play the role of the Lewis acids and the ligands are the bases. Reactions of the proton are a special subdivision of the general category.

While S_E reactions are known, as in the reaction of Hg^{2+} with $[Co(NH_3)_5Cl]^{2+}$, they are less important than S_N reactions. Two fundamentally different paths for the latter reaction can be visualized, the familiar S_N1 (dissociation) and S_N2 (displacement) mechanisms. In addition, several other, rather restricted, mechanisms are likely in certain cases, but the greater part of the effort expended in studying substitution reactions of complexes has been concerned with trying to assign S_N1 or S_N2 labels to them. This is a difficult task at best, since unequivocal evidence is hard to obtain. The strongest evidence would undoubtedly be the detection of the intermediate of reduced coordination number, M, which is characteristic of the S_N1 mechanism.

$$M-X \rightarrow M + X \tag{3}$$

$$M + Y \rightarrow M-Y \tag{4}$$

However the nature of M is generally such that it escapes detection by any direct means and subtle evidence for its presence or absence must be judged.†

In spite of the difficulties, the division mentioned above has been fruitful and a general discussion of the effect that changing variables can have on the rates and mechanisms, S_N1 or S_N2, of the reactions of complexes can be given. The variables that might be considered include the nature of the metal ion, the nature of the ligands, the nature of the external reagent, and the geometry and coordination number of the complex. To proceed, it is necessary to have a theory of energetics and binding in coordination compounds, so that differences in energy between the initial state and possible transition states may be at least roughly estimated. A very simple and remarkably useful theory is the old electrostatic one. This theory is most reliable for systems containing a positively charged central ion and charged or polar ligands where π bonding (double bonding) is not an important factor.

For example, the coordinate bond energy is defined as the heat of the following reaction in the vapor state:

$$ML^{m+}(g) \rightarrow M^{m+}(g) + L(g) \tag{5}$$

Experimentally coordinate bond energies range from about 15 kcal per bond in a complex such as $Rb(H_2O)_6{}^+$ to about 500 kcal per bond in $TiCl_4$. It is indeed remarkable that in simple cases, such as those given, a point charge electrostatic model will give theoretical bond energies in agreement with the experimental over such a wide range. However, on looking at a larger amount of data of all kinds, it becomes clear that more variables than the charge and size of ions are needed to explain their behavior. One important variable is found to be the number of d orbital electrons for the transition metal ions.

Crystal field theory‡ is applicable to any orderly arrangement of interacting particles to which it is reasonable to assign electrical charges or dipoles. A complex ion would be one example of such a system. The crystal field is the electric field acting at the central metal ion owing to the attached groups or ligands. This field has certain symmetry properties which greatly affect the energies of electrons, particularly in the various atomic d orbitals of the central ion. These

† In the S_N2 mechanism a species is formed of increased coordination number. This may be an activated complex (very unstable) or an intermediate (some stability). Both X and Y are bonded to M ($Y-M-X$).

‡ A convention widely used is that the term "crystal field theory" applies to the primarily electrostatic approach and the term "ligand field theory" to the combined electrostatic and molecular orbital method in which some covalent bonding is allowed for.

energy changes lead to consequences that have been of value in explaining the spectroscopic, magnetic, and thermodynamic properties of complex ions of the transition metals. A number of review articles discuss these properties in terms of the theory (*1, 2, 3, 4*).

Another important consequence of the splitting apart in energy of the several *d* orbitals is that the rates of reaction of similar compounds of metal ions with different numbers of *d* electrons are influenced strongly. The reason for this can be seen from the following considerations: the *d* electrons will occupy preferentially the lower-energy *d* orbitals. This makes the complex more stable than otherwise by an amount called the crystal field stabilization energy (CFSE). This energy difference can be estimated from spectroscopic data. It also shows up in the thermodynamic properties such as heats of hydration, lattice energies, and stability constants. In the case of a substitution reaction, for example, any reaction mechanism will change the coordination number and geometry of the original reactant as it passes into the transition state. Systems that were strongly crystal field stabilized will usually resist these changes, since it was the original coordination number and geometry which produced the CFSE.

This is particularly so for octahedral complexes containing three or eight *d* electrons and six *d* electrons in the special case of spin-pairing of these electrons. This shows up most dramatically in the special inertness toward substitution of complexes of chromium, cobalt, rhodium and iridium. In these cases very regular octahedral complexes tend to form which are difficult to distort for any reaction mechanism. The inertness is also helped by the high positive charge on the central ion.

For the divalent metal ions of the first transition series definite predictions can be made, by the use of crystal field theory, as to relative rates of reaction. The predictions are that rates of substitution will vary in the order Mn⟩Fe⟩ Co⟩Ni⟨Cu⟨Zn. In this listing ferrous ion is considered as spin-free (paramagnetic). If ferrous ion is spin-paired (diamagnetic), then, it is predicted to react the slowest of all.

The above predictions can be tested by looking at experimental data on rates of reaction or, even better, activation energies. The example of the *o*-phenanthroline and dipyridyl complexes is particularly useful, since the latter data are available for several of the ions. Table 5.1 shows some experimental rate data and some theoretical calculations of loss of CFSE for a number of such systems. The reaction studied is the rate of dissociation of one of the ligands from the indicated complex.

$$\text{Fe(phen)}_3^{++} \rightarrow \text{Fe(phen)}_2^{++} + \text{phen} \qquad (6)$$

These rates generally are obtained from the study of isotope exhange reactions. Such exchange reactions of, for instance, labeled phenanthroline with unlabeled phenanthroline have rates independent of the concentration of free ligand. Accordingly, they are considered to be $S_N 1$ (dissociation) reactions and the losses in CFSE are computed for a transition state in which only five groups instead of six are attached to each metal ion (the organic amines are bidentate ligands). The crystal field parameter Dq is found from spectral studies and is about 3–4 kcal/mole for these particular ligands attached to the divalent ions of the first transition series. It can be seen that low rates and high activation energies are found for the metal ions that have a large loss in CFSE.

TABLE 5.1. KINETIC DATA AND CRYSTAL FIELD STABILI-
ZATION ENERGY CHANGES FOR THE DISSOCIATION OF
BIVALENT METAL COMPLEXES OF PHENANTHROLINE
AND DIPYRIDYL AT 25°C[a]

Electronic System	$\Delta E(Dq)$[b]	Complex Ion	$k_{exch.}$ (min^{-1})	$E_{act.}$ (kcal mole^{-1})	$\Delta S\ddagger$ (eu)
d^3	2	V(phen)$_3^{++}$			
d^5	0	Mn(dipy)$_3^{++}$	fast		
d^6	4	Fe(phen)$_3^{++}$	0.0043	32.1	+28
		Fe(dipy)$_3^{++}$	0.0089	28.4	+17
d^7	0[c]	Co(phen)$_3^{++}$	12.66	20.6	+ 5
		Co(dipy)$_3^{++}$	fast		
d^8	2	Ni(phen)$_3^{++}$	0.0005	25.2	+ 1
		Ni(phen)$^{++}$	0.0011	23.1	− 5
		Ni(phen)$^{++}$	0.0005	26.2	+ 5
		Ni(dipy)$_3^{++}$	0.137	22.4	+ 2
d^9	0[c]	Cu(phen)$_3^{++}$	fast		
d^{10}	0	Zn(phen)$_3^{++}$	fast		

[a] Data from Ellis, P. and Wilkins, R. G., *J. Chem. Soc.* 1959: 299.
[b] Calculated as the difference in CFSE between an octahedral ground state and a square pyramid transition state.
[c] Jahn–Teller stabilization in ground state allowed for.

Most substitution reactions of these metal ions are very much faster and special methods must be used to follow them. A very interesting example is supplied by solvent exchange studies done by means of nuclear magnetic resonance (NMR) methods. It has been known for some time that paramagnetic ions will shorten the measured transverse (T_2) and longitudinal (T_1) relaxation times in NMR spectra. Recently it has been shown that the changes enable rate constants for exchange reactions of the following kind to be measured (5):

$$[Cu(H_2{}^*O)_6]^{++} + H_2O \rightleftharpoons [Cu(H_2O)_6]^{++} + H_2{}^*O \qquad (2)$$

The asterisk is simply used to indicate a solvent molecule bound initially to a paramagnetic ion to distinguish it from bulk solvent molecules. In general, one can measure either the lifetime, τ_B, of a water molecule bound to the ion or the lifetime, T_{2B}, of a nuclear spin state in a water molecule bound to the ion. Whichever time is longer will correspond to the rate determining step and will be measured. The reciprocal of τ_B is the first-order rate constant for the forward step of reaction (2).

Table 5.2 presents some exchange data obtained in water and in methanol solutions of some paramagnetic ions. In most cases only lower limits can be put on the rate constants because of the possibility that T_{2B} is rate controlling. Even so, the data are tremendously valuable in that for the first time it is possible to get some idea of the permanence of a solvent molecule bound to the simpler ions. For some cases, such as copper II and nickel II in methanol, it is clear

TABLE 5.2. LOWER LIMITS TO EXCHANGE RATE CONSTANTS, I/τ_B, FOR PARAMAGNETIC IONS IN WATER AND METHANOL AT 25°C

Ion	CH$_3$OH[a,b]	CH$_3$OH[a]	H$_2$O[c]
Cr^{3+}	1.1×10^4	3.2×10^3	slow
Fe^{3+}	3.2×10^4	2.2×10^4	$1 \times 10^{4(d)}$
Mn^{++}	2.5×10^5	1.8×10^4	3×10^7
Fe^{++}	——	——	3×10^6
Co^{++}	1.1×10^4	1.7×10^3	1×10^6
Ni^{++}	2.6×10^3	2.2×10^3	3×10^4
Cu^{++}	1.0×10^4	1.0×10^4	1×10^4 equatorial[e]
			2×10^8 axial[e]

[a] Data from ref. (6).
[b] All rate constants in sec^{-1}. The underlined atoms are the nuclei whose exchange rate (or rate of relaxation) is being measured.
[c] Data from ref. (7).
[d] H. Taube, private communication.
[e] Evidence for two kinds of coordinate water molecules.

that the rate of solvent exchange is being measured, since the rates are the same for the methyl protons and for the hydroxyl protons. This would not be true if T_{2B} were being measured.

It is of considerable interest that methyl alcohol molecules are exchanged more slowly than water molecules. This is either because they are held more firmly or because the methyl group offers steric hindrance to an incoming solvent molecule in an S_N2-like process. The very high lability of solvent attached to iron III is noteworthy. The results are probably complicated by the fact that, even in the acid solutions where the spectra were taken, some $[Fe(H_2O)_5OH]^{++}$ will exist, and it is known that the hydroxy group is usually strongly labilizing for substitution reactions (8). Even so, the water exchange rate constant is clearly very much greater than for an ion such as $[Cr(H_2O)_6]^{3+}$ where τ_B is about 10^6 seconds instead of 10^{-4}. This is an extreme example of crystal field stabilization in the latter ion.

Table 5.3 presents some data on the sulfation reaction obtained by Eigen (9) using ultrasonic relaxation spectroscopy. It is strongly indicated by the results that the process of forming a sulfato complex from an aquo complex consists of several stages. The first of these are concerned with the diffusion controlled formation of an ion pair or outer-sphere complex.

$$[M(H_2O)_6]^{++} + SO_4^= \rightleftarrows [M(H_2O)_6]^{++}, SO_4^= \qquad (7)$$

The last stage, and the one of chemical interest, is the rearrangement of this ion pair to the true complex.

$$[M(H_2O)_6]^{++}, SO_4^= \underset{k_2}{\overset{k_1}{\rightleftarrows}} [M(H_2O)_5SO_4] + H_2O \qquad (8)$$

The results show the expected dependence on electrostatic factors, since small cations react more slowly than similar but larger ions. The transition metal ions show the expected order manganese II⟩cobalt II⟩nickel II⟨copper II⟨zinc II.

TABLE 5.3. RATE CONSTANTS FOR REACTION $[M(H_2O)_n]^{++}$, $A = \underset{k_2}{\overset{k_1}{\rightleftarrows}}$ $[M(H_2O)_{n-1}A] + H_2O$ AT 25°C[a]

M	A	k_1, sec^{-1}	k_2, sec^{-1}
Be^{++}	SO$_4^=$	1×10^2	1.3×10^3
Mg^{++}	SO$_4^=$	1×10^5	8×10^5
Ca^{++}	SO$_4^{=(b)}$	$(10^7)^{(c)}$	$(10^8)^{(c)}$
Mg^{++}	S$_2$O$_3^{=(b)}$	1×10^5	1.5×10^6
Mg^{++}	CrO$_4^{=(b)}$	1×10^5	1.5×10^6
Zn^{++}	SO$_4^=$	1×10^5	1×10^7
Cu^{++}	SO$_4^=$	$(10^8)^{(c)}$	1×10^6
Ni^{++}	SO$_4^=$	1×10^4	1×10^5
Co^{++}	SO$_4^=$	2×10^5	2.5×10^6
Mn^{++}	SO$_4^=$	4×10^6	2×10^7

[a] Data from ref. (9).
[b] Note that some data for anions other than sulfate are also given.
[c] The numbers in parentheses are relatively uncertain.

Two other features are especially noteworthy: one is that the rate constant k_1 is apparently independent of the anion associated with the cation, and the other is that the value of k_1 is remarkably similar to the rate constants for water exchange given in Table 5.2. This seems to be very powerful evidence for an S_N1 or dissociation mechanism operating in all these cases, so that the rate step is the loss of a water molecule from the first coordination shell of the cation. Apparently, the anion gives very little assistance in pushing off the leaving group.

As a final example of labile systems, we may quote some recent data (10) on the rate of exchange of glycine, methylglycine (sarcosine), and dimethylglycine with metal ions studied by NMR line broadening methods. Table 5.4 gives the rate constants, or limits to the rate constants, as calculated from both the CH_2 peak and the averaged OH–NH peak. A negative temperature dependence shows that a rate of magnetic relaxation is being measured $(1/T_{2B})$ and a positive temperature dependence shows that chemical exchange is being measured.

There are two important points in Table 5.4. One is that the exchange reactions of copper II are always second order, the rate depending directly on the concentration of free glycine anion. Thus, for the reaction

$$Cu(gly^*)_2 + gly^- \rightleftarrows Cu(gly)_2 + gly^{*-} \tag{9}$$

we have

$$1/\tau_B = k_2[gly^-].$$

This suggests an S_N2 mechanism in agreement with the square planar or tetragonal structure of copper II complexes. Thus, for the planar complexes of

TABLE 5.4. RATE LIMITS FOR THE EXCHANGE OF GLYCINES AT $27°C^{(a)}$

Complex	k_1 or k_2, sec^{-1}	Temp. dependence, kcal
Cu(gly)$_2$	$k_{OH} = 8.2 \times 10^6 M^{-1}$	$E_a = 6$
	$k_{CH_2} = 2.6 \times 10^6 M^{-1}$	$E_a = 6$
Ni(gly)$_3^-$	$k_{OH} < 1 \times 10^{3(b)}$ •	negative
	$k_{CH_2} < 3 \times 10^{2(b)}$	positive
Co(gly)$_3^-$	$k_{OH} = 5.7 \times 10^3 + 4.8 \times 10^3 M^{-1}$	$E_a = 10$
	$k_{CH_2} = 5.7 \times 10^3 + 3.8 \times 10^3 M^{-1}$	$E_a = 10$
Mn(gly)$_2$	$k_{OH} > 1 \times 10^5$	negative
	$k_{CH_2} > 1 \times 10^4$	negative
Fe(gly)$_2$	$k_{OH} = 2.2 \times 10^4 + 5 \times 10^4 M^{-1}$	$E_a = 9.5$
	$k_{CH_2} = 2.2 \times 10^4 + 3.2 \times 10^4 M^{-1}$	$E_a = 9.5$
Cu(sarc)$_2$	$k_{OH} = 6 \times 10^5 M^{-1}$	$E_a = 7$
Ni(sarc)$_3^-$	$k_{CH_2} = 60 + 1 \times 10^2 M^{-1}$	positive$^{(c)}$
Co(sarc)$_3^-$	$k_{OH} = 6.7 \times 10^2 + 3.3 \times 10^3 M^{-1}$	$E_a = 13$
	$k_{CH_2} = 4.2 \times 10^2 + 2.1 \times 10^2 M^{-1}$	$E_a = 13$
Cu(dmg)$_2$	$k_{CH_2} = 1.3 \times 10^4 M^{-1}$	$E_a = 9.5$
Ni(dmg)$_3^-$	$k_{CH_2} = 70 + 4.7 \times 10^2 M^{-1}$	$E_a = 17$
Co(dmg)$_3^-$	$k_{CH_2} = 3.2 \times 10^2 + 7.3 \times 10^3 M^{-1}$	positive

(a) Data from ref. (10).
(b) Wilkins, R. G. and Shamsuddin Ahmad, A. K., *Proc. Chem. Soc.* **399** (1959), give $k_1 = 10$ sec^{-1} for uncatalyzed dissociation.
(c) Rate constant is at 54°C.

platinum II, S_N2 mechanisms have always been found (11). This assignment is supported by the rate sequence glycine>sarcosine>dimethylglycine, which is expected because of increasing steric hindrance in forming the transition state. Similar steric retardation is known for platinum II complexes (11).

For octahedral cobalt II and nickel II quite different results are found.

$$Ni(gly*)_3^- + gly^- \rightleftarrows Ni(gly)_3^- + gly*^- \qquad (10)$$

For example, the rate sequence is now dimethylglycine⟩sarcosine glycine. This is the order expected for an S_N1 mechanism where steric strain in the initial state produces an acceleration of dissociation processes (12). Also, the exchange reactions are mixed first and second order, $1/\tau_B = k_1 + k_2(gly^-)$. Such a rate law can be explained very nicely by a dissociation mechanism for a chelate ligand (10). Account must be taken of the intermediate in which only one end (the carboxylate) of the chelate has been released. This intermediate will reclose many times before the amine end also dissociates.

The S_N2 mechanism for planar copper II probably involves an intermediate (or possibly a transition state) with a trigonal bipyramid structure. There will be some loss of CFSE in forming such a structure, perhaps $2Dq$ units. However, the metal–ligand attractions and ligand–ligand repulsions will be very favorable otherwise.

In the case of the highly hindered 2,3-diamino-2,3-dimethylbutane (tetramethylethylenediamine or tetraMeen) both nickel and copper add only two molecules of ligands, forming square complexes. The nickel complex, for example, is diamagnetic, as expected in a square complex. Here, where similar mechanisms may be expected for both metal ions, measurements of the dissociation rates show that the copper complex reacts 2000 times faster than the nickel complex at 0°C (13). The activation energy for nickel II is four kcal higher than for copper II. This is in the direction predicted by crystal field theory.

The well-studied examples of cobalt III, a d^6 system, and chromium III, a d^3 system, provide much of the available data on substitution reactions of octahedral complexes. The slowness of these reactions, e.g., the acid hydrolysis or aquation reaction,

$$[Co(NH_3)_5Cl]^{2+} + H_2O \rightleftarrows [Co(NH_3)_5H_2O]^{3+} + Cl^- \qquad (11)$$

is a consequence of the small size and high charge of the metal ion on the one hand, and very large ligand field effects on the other. The same factors enter into the even slower reactions of the analogous d^6 compounds $[Rh(NH_3)_5Cl]^{2+}$ and $[Ir(NH_3)_5Cl]^{2+}$. Since the Rh^{3+} and Ir^{3+} ions are larger than Co^{3+}, it would be difficult to account for the greater difficulty of hydrolysis if it were not for the corrections to the simple electrostatic theory. However, the second and third transition series ions have higher effective charges than cobalt and larger crystal field effects. Thus, it is known from spectroscopic data that Dq for iridium is almost twice as large as for cobalt.

Let us consider further some of the kinetic consequences of the d orbital electrons in these examples. The six d electrons fill up the octahedral faces with a cloud of charge extending well out from the central atom. They represent a formidable barrier to an S_N2 attack by an electron-donating, or nucleophilic, reagent, since it is just these open faces that might be considered the logical points of entry for such reagents. Furthermore, the d energy levels of Table 5.5 (p. 106), can help us predict something about the geometry and coordination number of probable transition states or intermediates. For example, an incoming reagent in earlier days was often thought of as attacking at an octahedral edge and forming a transition state with five groups in a plane. This would be a pentagonal bipyramid. The energy levels of such a system when filled with six electrons give a CFSE of $15.5Dq$, as compared to $24Dq$ in the original complex. This represents a loss of $8.5Dq$ which would contribute to the activation energy. The energy loss is so large as to make this particular reaction route impractical.

If an S_N1 mechanism operates, two probable geometries for the intermediate of coordination number five would be formed—the square pyramid and the trigonal pyramid. It can again be calculated that the energy levels of the trigonal bipyramid are not favorable for six d electrons. Only in the special case that one of the remaining five ligands is an electron-donating group (π bonding) does such a rearrangement become plausible since strong π bonding to the metal is possible only in the trigonal form.§ The removal of one group, leaving the others undisturbed, produces the least perturbation of the electronic energy levels and the least loss of CFSE. This would be the square pyramid intermediate. If the chloride ion is removed from $[Co(NH_3)_5Cl]^{2+}$ to form $[Co(NH_3)_5]^{3+}$, for example, it is very unlikely that this species could survive even a few molecular collisions with such a vacant position in its coordination shell. Instead, the first available molecule or ion that can act as a ligand will fill up the vacant spot. In fact, using thermochemical data and the electrostatic model as a basis for calculation, it is easy to show that it is not possible to form $[Co(NH_3)_5]^{3+}$ in any geometry without an excessive expenditure of energy. That is, the coordinate bond energy,

$$[Co(NH_3)_5Cl]^{2+} \rightarrow [Co(NH_3)_5]^{3+} + Cl^- \qquad (12)$$

is simply too large—about 94 kcal per mole in solution for a square pyramid structure.

Since the experimental activation energy for the acid hydrolysis reaction is only 24 kcal, it is necessary to find a lower energy path. This creates a visualization of the mechanism of reaction of such an ion as one in which the Co–Cl bond is lengthened to some critical distance, at which point a solvent molecule slips in to occupy the place of the chloride ion, which is then expelled. The transition state is seven-coordinated with five groups in a square pyramid and the entering and leaving groups at a longer distance and adjacent to each other. Fig. 5.1 shows such a structure for the reaction of an octahedral rhodium III complex.

§ The repulsion between the five ligands is less in a trigonal bipyramid than in a square pyramid. However, ligand field effects often overshadow this.

N. S. Hush has recently calculated the crystal field energy levels for such an intermediate (*14*). The interesting result is that the losses in CFSE in forming the seven-coordinated intermediate are very similar to those for forming a five-coordinated, square pyramid intermediate. In fact, if anything, the losses are somewhat less, indicating that this is a very favorable structure for substitution reactions of metal complexes.

Table 5.5 gives the theoretical one-electron energies of the different *d* orbitals in regular complexes of several different geometries as, calculated by Ballhausen and Klixbull Jørgensen (*1*) and by Hush (*14*). These are the basis for the various

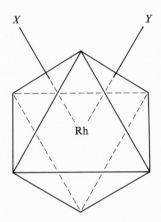

FIGURE 5.1.
Seven-coordinated transition state for rhodium III complexes. *X* and *Y* are leaving and entering groups.

estimates of crystal field activation energy which have been quoted. All that is needed is to know the structure of the ground state, to assume a structure for the transition state, and to feed *d* electrons into the various levels with due regard for possible spin-pairing.

It must be appreciated, however, that the energies given are based upon a much oversimplified model in which only electrostatic perturbations are taken into account and many other important effects are ignored. It would be remarkable indeed if quantitative agreement with experiment was obtained. Table 5.5 can only be used as a rough guide for estimating the probable magnitude of the effects. For example, Hush's intermediate gives very anomalous predictions in certain cases. For a spin-free d^6 system such as $[Fe(H_2O)_6]^{2+}$, the ground-state CFSE may be estimated as $4.57 Dq$ units considered as a slightly distorted octahedron. The transition state has a CFSE of $6.08 Dq$, according to Table 5.5.

This predicts a negative contribution to the activation energy and extreme lability for iron II aquo ion. In fact, from Table 5.2 the iron II is not as labile as manganese II, nor is its activation energy any different from that of manganese II or cobalt II in water exchange (7). Unfortunately, it cannot be said whether this represents a failure for the theory or a poor choice of structure for the transition state.

TABLE 5.5. THE d ORBITAL ENERGY LEVELS IN CRYSTAL FIELDS OF DIFFERENT SYMMETRIES

C.N.	Structure	$d_{x^2-y^2}$	d_{z^2}	d_{xy}	d_{xz}	d_{yz}
1	...[b]	$-3.14\ Dq$	$5.14\ Dq$	$-3.14\ Dq$	$0.57\ Dq$	$0.57\ Dq$
2	linear[b]	-6.28	10.28	-6.28	1.14	1.14
3	trigonal[c]	5.46	-3.21	5.46	-3.86	-3.86
4	tetrahedral	-2.67	-2.67	1.78	1.78	1.78
4	square planar[c]	12.28	-4.28	2.28	-5.14	-5.14
5	trigonal bipyramid[d]	-0.82	7.07	-0.82	-2.72	-2.72
5	square pyramid[d]	9.14	0.86	-0.86	-4.57	-4.57
6	octahedron	6.00	6.00	-4.00	-4.00	-4.00
7	pentagonal bipyramid[d]	2.82	4.93	2.82	-5.28	-5.28
7	Hush's intermediate	8.79	1.39[e]	-1.51[e]	-2.60[f]	-6.08[f]

[a] Data from ref. (*1*) and (*14*).
[b] Bonds lie along z axis.
[c] Bonds in the xy plane.
[d] Pyramid base in xy plane.
[e] d_{z^2}, d_{xy} hybrids.
[f] d_{xz}, d_{yz} hybrids.

The experimental activation energy for chromium III complexes undergoing hydrolysis runs about 2 kcal less than for cobalt III. Also, for rhodium III complexes the activation energies are about 2 kcal more than for cobalt III. These are in the direction predicted by crystal field theory, but the size of the differences is only about half or less of what is expected. The prediction, how-ever, depends on assuming an identical geometry for the transition state in each case and this assumption may be seriously in error. For example, the degree of solvent participation in an intermediate such as Fig. 5.1 may increase in going from one metal to another. Also, differences in the amount of covalent bonding between the first transition series and the second and third may affect the activation energies. To sum up, the over-all rates and activation energies are determined by many factors, of which crystal field effects are only one.

REFERENCES

1. F. Basolo and R. G. Pearson, *Mechanisms of Inorganic Reactions*, Wiley, New York, 1958, chap. 2.
2. T. M. Dunn, "The Visible and Ultra-violet Spectra of Complex Compounds," in J. Lewis and R. Wilkins (eds.), *Modern Coordination Chemistry*, Interscience, New York, 1960, chap. IV.
3. P. George and D. S. McClure, "The Effect of Inner Orbital Splitting on the Thermodynamic Properties of Transition Metal Compounds and Coordination Complexes," in F. A. Cotton (ed.), *Progress in Inorganic Chemistry*, Interscience, New York, 1959, chap. 6.
4. W. E. Moffitt and C. J. Ballhausen, *Ann. Rev. Phys. Chem.* **7**: 107 (1956).
5. H. M. McConnell and S. B. Berger, *J. Chem. Phys.* **27**: 230 (1957).
6. R. G. Pearson, J. W. Palmer, M. M. Anderson, and A. L. Allred, *Z. Elektrochem.* **64**: 110 (1960).
7. T. J. Swift and R. E. Connick, *J. Chem. Phys.* **37**: 307 (1962).
8. R. G. Pearson and F. Basolo, *J. Am. Chem. Soc.* **78**: 4878 (1956).
9. M. Eigen, *Z. Elektrochem.* **64**: 115 (1960); **66**: 107 (1962).
10. R. G. Pearson and R. D. Lanier, *J. Am. Chem. Soc.*, in press.
11. F. Basolo and R. G. Pearson, in F. A. Cotton (ed.), *Progress in Inorganic Chemistry*, Interscience, New York, 1962.
12. R. G. Pearson, F. Basolo, and C. R. Boston, *J. Am. Chem. Soc.* **74**: 2943 (1952).
13. R. G. Wilkins, *J. Chem. Soc.* **1957**: 4521.
14. N. S. Hush, *Austral. J. Chem.* **15**: 378 (1962).

INDEX

Format by Faith Nicholas
Set in Monotype Times Roman
Composed by Santype Limited
Printed by The Murray Printing Company
Bound by The Haddon Craftsmen, Inc.
HARPER & ROW, PUBLISHERS, INCORPORATED